# GEORGE ROGERS CLARK

## SOLDIER AND HERO

*Other Books by Jeannette Covert Nolan*

# GEORGE ROGERS CLARK

## SOLDIER AND HERO
*(November 19, 1752 – February 13, 1818)*

## BY JEANNETTE COVERT NOLAN

### ILLUSTRATED BY LEE AMES

**JULIAN MESSNER, INC.**

NEW YORK

Published by Julian Messner, Inc.
8 West 40th Street, New York 18
Published Simultaneously in Canada
By The Copp Clark Company, Ltd.

Library of Congress Catalog Card No. 54-10592

Third Printing, 1957

*For my friends, Jane and Elizabeth
Veatch, with best wishes and admiration.*

**J. C. N.**

# CONTENTS

# CONTENTS

# GEORGE ROGERS CLARK

## SOLDIER AND HERO

# AN EVENING PARTY, 1772

*"Green grow the rushes, O!*
*Kiss her quick and let her go!*
*But don't you muss her ruffles, O!"*

In the big parlor of his father's Virginia plantation house George Rogers Clark was dancing with his sister Ann. Round and round they whirled, the tall, red-haired young man and the slender, pretty girl, swaying, skipping, weaving skillfully in and out among the other youthful dancers.

The windows of the room were open to the warm August evening. The bearskin rugs had been rolled back from the pine-planked floor. Candles shed rings of wavering yellow light into the corner where the fiddlers busily scraped their bows and beat the measure of the tune with their boot heels.

*"Green grow the rushes, O!—"*

George was enjoying the party. He could scarcely realize that only yesterday he had arrived home, that only a week ago he had been tramping through the depths of the western wilderness. Glancing about him, he was pleased to see his brother Jonathan seated on a bench, watching the dancing. It pleased him to know that his father was just outside, on the lawn, a leisurely, amiable host, smoking a clay-stemmed pipe, and that his mother was in the kitchen, supervising the mixing of a bowl of punch. He had enjoyed the delicious supper spread by the Negro servants on the white-draped table —those platters of baked ham and turkey, the fruit pies and fluffy cakes. And he was flattered that so many of the Clark and Rogers relatives had come from their near-by farms to the party in his honor tonight.

Indeed, the house and the plantation had never

seamed safer, more comfortable. It was fun to be here.

"But safety and comfort aren't the things I want most," he said to himself. "I won't stay. I can't!"

*"Kiss her quick and let her go—"*

Minding the music, George bent and kissed Ann's flushed cheek. Then, as the tune ended, he swung toward Jonathan's bench.

"Have a seat, Ann," he said. "Your face is red, you're breathless."

"And no wonder!" Ann dropped down beside Jonathan. "I do declare, George, you're the liveliest stepper in Caroline County. You just put your whole soul into it, don't you?"

"George puts his whole soul into everything he tackles," said Jonathan, smiling.

The fiddlers had risen and, with the other dancers, were trailing into the kitchen for refreshments. George drew a handkerchief from his pocket.

"Your face is red as a radish. Better mop it," he said. "But you admit that I'm a *good* stepper, Ann?"

"I admit that you haven't forgotten how to dance— not quite. You haven't yet changed into a savage, an Indian in war paint and feathers, brandishing a toma- hawk." Ann was obediently scrubbing her moist fore- head with George's handkerchief. "I was afraid you would. Oh, don't laugh! I daresay it could happen, if you went away too often."

"And you wouldn't like it?"

"Heavens, no! I'd hate it. Indians terrify me. George,"

she said, looking sternly up at him, "you're not thinking of leaving home *again?*"

"Well, I—"

"*Are* you?"

He hesitated. Of course he was thinking of leaving again. He had thought of it every minute since his return from the long exciting journey to the forks of the Ohio River, his forty-four days and hundreds of miles on the streams and in the forest. He had been born a wanderer; travel and adventure had always been his heart's desire. Now that he was nineteen and had seen the West, he would never be content anywhere else!

But could he explain this to Ann, to his family? He was fond of his sisters and brothers. Jonathan, Ann, John, Richard, Edmund, Lucy, Elizabeth, William and baby Frances—he loved them all; and his parents, too. How could he make them understand that, dear as they were to him, the call of distant places, the free life of the wilderness (yes, even danger and loneliness) were dearer still?

"George!" Ann exclaimed. "Why don't you answer?"

"Well, I—I—"

The fiddlers interrupted. Reappearing they took up their bows and launched into a rollicking reel tune. The dancers reassembled; and George saw with relief that his mother was crossing the floor, neat and brisk in a white cap and starchy apron, a very small boy tugging at her flounced skirts.

"Here's Mother," George said. "And William."

Jonathan got to his feet. "Mother's coming to dance the reel with me. She promised. George, will you tend to William?"

14

"Oh, yes," George said. "William and I are great chums."

"And much alike," Jonathan observed. "The same carrot-colored hair, the same stubborn streak."

"Stubborn? Nonsense! Hello, Mother," George said. "Hello, William. You're going out on the lawn with me."

"Yes, do take him out, George," Mrs. Clark said, smiling. "He has stuffed himself with cake and spilled punch on his pinafore. He's sleepy and ought to be in bed."

"No!" said William. "I'm *not* sleepy."

"Ah, then you'll be a proper gentleman and go quietly." George stooped and lifted the little boy to his shoulder "I suppose you have a partner for the reel, Ann?"

"I think so," Ann said. "One of the Rogers cousins. But, George, you haven't told me—"

"Later," he said. "Later."

"Don't fuss, Ann," Jonathan advised. "George can't leave without Father's consent. And whatever Father decides will be right."

George carried William out to the cool, shadowy yard where his father and a group of older men sat in a friendly circle, their pipes glowing in the darkness. He was vaguely worried by what Jonathan had said—for it was true enough. Ann's queries might be dodged or ignored; but it was true that George could not start again for the West without his father's consent.

I'll have to talk with Father tomorrow, George thought. I wonder what he *will* decide.

George sat down on the grass and William promptly went to sleep in his lap.

The night was peaceful, the sky studded with stars,

a breeze rustling the treetops. Patches of candlelight and the strains of gay music drifted from the house. A yellow moon climbed lazily above the black roofs of the barns and stables; and from the chimneys of the slave cabins spiraled thin wisps of fragrant wood smoke.

But the conversation of John Clark and his guests was not peaceful; it concerned the struggle of the American colonies with England, their feeling of restlessness and resentment. Not that the feeling was new—or the struggle, either. No, for years the colonists here in Virginia and everywhere in America had been protesting against the harsh laws and heavy taxes imposed upon them by the English king. For years, through their legislatures, they had begged for some easing of their burdens.

The king's method of dealing with such petitions had been simple, though drastic. He had made the laws harsher, the taxes heavier and had stationed his soldiers in the colonies to see that his royal will prevailed.

Tonight on John Clark's lawn the many grievances of the colonists were discussed. From time to time there had been incidents of rebellion:

"Incidents for which we were punished," said one man. "Punished like naughty children. Wasn't it three years ago that our own Virginia legislature, the House of Burgesses, passed the Virginia Resolves? Yes, and what did the king do? He had the legislature dissolved! Yet what we asked was only the fair treatment to which we're entitled, as British subjects."

"We resolve—and the king *dissolves*," John Clark commented, puffing at his pipe.

"We are oppressed," said another man. "The king and

16

his governors and ministers have no respect for us. A bad attitude!—what can it do but breed more and worse rebellions?"

A third man said that the quarrel between king and colonies might be mended, even now: "The king could mend it, if he wished to."

"The king knows very little about us; that's the stumbling block," said John Clark. "He has never seen us. He prefers not to heed what our best spokesmen tell him about us. And he seems to lack the imagination to picture us as we really are. Once we *were* like children; the colonies our ancestors founded in America were small and dependent. But now we're big, prosperous, vigorous, able to govern ourselves. When a boy becomes a man, he can't be held on leading strings. He wants to strike out for himself, and the wise parent will allow him to do so."

The voices droned on, as the men conjectured what was in store for them as Virginians, as Americans.

Perhaps the king would finally alter his mistaken policies. Or perhaps not—and what then? Some people were frankly anticipating a day of crisis, a day when the thirteen colonies might unite in demanding the respect, the fair treatment and independence they wanted and deserved.

Was that day inevitable? Was it approaching? . . .

George had been listening keenly, for he had puzzled over these matters himself; he had ideas about them. He knew the spirit of his Virginia kinsmen; they would not tolerate oppression forever. And more than any of them, more even than his father, George was aware of Amer-

17

ica's immense size, how it stretched from the Atlantic seaboard inland, so far that its farthest limits could only be guessed at.

America, George thought, was too vast, too rough and lusty to be dominated by a tyrannical monarch on a prim, foreign throne.

"Liberty," George murmured. "We've got to have it —and we surely will!"

But mostly he was thinking of what his father had said about leading strings, and how this affected his own future. Wasn't John Clark a wise parent? And wasn't George the boy who had become a man?

Of course!

Therefore, thought George, Father will consent to-morrow, when I talk with him. In a week or two I'll be on the road again, westward bound.

William wakened then. Wriggling and rubbing his eyes, William said he must be carried back to his mother and the cake and punch.

"Oh, very well. You've had a nice nap, and the reel's over. William," George said, "do you know the Clark family's motto?"

William yawned and shook his head.

"You've never heard it?"

"No," said William drowsily.

"Would you like to hear it now?"

"No."

"You wouldn't?" George laughed. "I'll tell you, any-way. The Clark motto, William, is 'Do justice and fear not.' I'm going to remember it, and I hope you will, too."

18

# 2

## WESTWARD BOUND

It was morning and Mr. Clark was reading the *Virginia Gazette* when George came into the room. Mr. Clark laid the newspaper on his desk and looked up over the steel rims of his spectacles.

"So you have something to ask me, George?" he said.

"Yes, sir."

"What is it, my boy?"

George had rehearsed his speech. He had even dreamed about it. Now he poured it all out, his love of the West, his determination to live there.

He told his father that on his former journey he had trudged across the Blue Ridge Mountains, through the Shenandoah valley and the Alleghenies. In the frontier town of Pittsburgh he had chanced upon a missionary to the Indians, who was embarking on a voyage down the Ohio River. With the clergyman he had paddled in a canoe to the mouth of the Kanawha River, camped briefly and then turned back.

"This time I would go alone, Father, and by a shorter route," he said. "The land drained by the Ohio is beautiful and fertile, and open to anyone who claims it. I have that box of surveying instruments and the telescope Grandfather Rogers gave me. I've had a little experience at surveying. I'd pick out a fine tract of the land and survey it. I'd notch trees to mark it and put up some kind of shelter. After a year the land would be mine."

Mr. Clark nodded. "Would you cultivate and farm this tract?"

"Well, I'd clear it, anyway." George paused. "And I would probably do some exploring in Kentucky."

"Kentucky?" Mr. Clark said. "The section of Virginia beyond the mountains?"

"Yes, sir. The Iroquois and Cherokee tribes call it the Dark and Bloody Ground. They insist it belongs to them; and they've driven out or murdered the white men who tried to settle on it. But Daniel Boone, the great scout

20

and hunter, has explored parts of Kentucky. I'd like to
see it, too."

Mr. Clark nodded again. Perhaps he was remembering
his words of last night. Perhaps he regretted the words
and had never meant them to apply to his own family.
He was a proud man, proud of his six sons and four
daughters, and happiest when they were near him. But
he was also an unselfish man, and the happiness of his
children seemed to him even more valuable.

"You think, George, that the West is the place for
you?" he said.

"Yes, sir. I'm sure it is. I feel it in my bones! Of course,
I wouldn't be gone forever, Father. I'd be coming home
occasionally—maybe often."

"I hope so. And I suppose," Mr. Clark said slowly, "I
can't refuse you. You may go; you have my blessing."

That very day George began to make his plans—and to
talk about them. At the dinner table, in the evenings, he
talked of the West. Frenchmen, he said, had been the
first white people there. French trappers and priests had
ranged down from Canada, pushing frail boats through a
chain of lakes and rivers, stopping at various points to
erect log forts and trading posts. A Frenchman, Robert
Cavelier, the Sieur de La Salle, had discovered the Mississippi River, forged the entire length of the mighty
stream and taken possession of its vast valley in the name
of the king of France.

"Somehow the Indians never bothered the French
much," George said. "But they've hated the English who
went west. I don't know why."

"I know," Mr. Clark said. "It's because the Indians

thought of the French trappers and priests as transients who would soon move on. The English were invaders of a different sort—homemakers. The Indians saw that if the English stayed they would chop down the forests, till the soil, build roads and towns. So the savages have fought them tooth and nail."

"But, Father," Ann said, "that's civilization."

Mr. Clark smiled. "Yes, and the Indians never have wanted civilization."

"What the Indians want is for everything to be just as it's always been," said George.

Mr. Clark could recall the time, not so long ago, when France and England had been at war in Europe. The war had spread to America and the Indians had sided with the French.

"The king sent an army from England," he said, "and the colonies were required to furnish additional troops. Virginia raised three companies. Colonel George Washington was in charge of the Virginia troops—and a braver soldier never stood in boot leather!"

"And we won the war, didn't we?" Ann asked.

"Yes, England won it—finally, and at great cost." Mr. Clark looked thoughtful. "The French and Indian War had some odd results. It showed the colonies that they could muster an army here in America, with splendid officers to command the men. Another result was that France had to surrender all her territory to England and withdraw her soldiers from this continent. But the French inhabitants of those little scattered forts and trading posts haven't liked knuckling under to their English conquerors."

22

"And one more result is that the Indians are still scrapping with us," George said. "They don't know the war is over."

"Oh, George, I wish you weren't going out among the Indians," sighed Mrs. Clark.

"I'll be careful, Mother."

"He'll probably marry a squaw," Ann grumbled, "and have a brood of papooses."

"Ann is romantic," Jonathan said, laughing. "Now that she's sixteen she thinks of nothing but getting married."

"Well, *I* don't," George asserted. "I never think of it and I'll bet a shilling I *never* marry."

"But why not?" Ann said. "You're not that ugly. You have blue eyes, a sweet smile, broad shoulders. You're almost handsome, George."

"Bosh! Stuff and nonsense!"

"It's strange about the West," Mrs. Clark said musingly. "When my father—your Grandfather Rogers—came to Caroline County from his plantation on Virginia's coast, this was the West. Now this is the East."

"My dear wife," said Mr. Clark, "the West recedes steadily. It's always the place that's farther on, over the horizon."

At bedtime of George's last night at home, Jonathan made a suggestion.

Jonathan was the oldest of John Clark's sons; he was twenty-one, two years older than George. The two brothers had been comrades since childhood, working together in the fields and, when work was done, sharing the fun of neighborhood picnics, barbecues, fox hunts and shooting matches.

23

"I'll miss you, George," Jonathan said. "And I've been thinking. It won't be easy for you to tell the folks good-by. It might help to cheer you up if I left with you. I could take you part way—to the Blue Ridge foothills."

George was pleased. Despite his eagerness to be off, he had dreaded the farewells.

"But why don't you go all the way?" he said. "The western country would amaze you, Jonathan. People will soon be swarming to it, like bees to a molasses jug."

Jonathan shook his head. "No, I'd be a misfit in the wilderness. I haven't your taste for pioneering. And besides, I feel that my duty is here in Caroline County."

"Duty? Father has the other boys. Richard is twelve and frisky as a colt. Richard could do the chores."

"Oh, Richard's a stanch lad," Jonathan said. "But it's not the chores I'm thinking of. It's something else, more important."

George had reason to be grateful for Jonathan's suggestion. Breakfast next morning was a dismal meal. The younger children gazed soberly at George; Ann plagued him with questions; his mother and father were looking grave. Even William, perched on Mrs. Clark's knee, frowned solemnly into his porridge bowl, as if to show that this was no ordinary day.

"George," Mr. Clark said, "you'll have to pay a fee for registering any land you stake. Have you the money for that?"

"Yes, sir," George replied.

"George, you *will* write to us?" said Mrs. Clark.

"Yes, ma'am. I'll send a letter whenever I can."

"And tell us if you marry an Indian?" said Ann.

"You're not eating a thing, George. Aren't you hungry?" asked Richard.

Then Jonathan got up and grasped George by the arm and whisked him to the door. "Come on!" Jonathan exclaimed. "We've got to make tracks!"

In a moment the farewells had been said, then they were striding out of the house, through the yard, turning at the gate to wave.

"Whew, that was awful!" George groaned.

"But we managed it."

"You managed it, Jonathan—and my thanks to you."

The morning was hot and sunny. The dusty road ran between fenced meadows of grazing cattle and fields of ripening corn. They walked at a regular, swinging pace. Both had rifles slung on their shoulders, bullet pouch and powder horn dangling from their belts. George had also an ax, a new long-bladed knife, his surveyor's kit and a knapsack.

"Except for our equipment, it's like the time when we were little duffers in pantaloons, starting out for Uncle Donald Robertson's school at Dunkirk," Jonathan remarked presently.

George grinned. "Don't remind me of Dunkirk. What a wretched failure I was there!"

"Because you wouldn't study," Jonathan said. "Poor Uncle Donald, a merry chase you led him, traipsing off to the woods, playing truant."

"Poor Uncle Donald, indeed!" mocked George. "I was better to him than he deserved. He had a birch rod tipped with metal. I can feel Uncle Donald's rod now, swishing the air, stinging the seat of my breeches."

25

"He was ambitious for you," Jonathan said. "His prize pupil was James Madison. Uncle Donald wanted you to be as smart as James Madison."

"And I wasn't."

"You could have been, by studying a bit. You threw your books in the duck pond."

"Well, I wasn't interested in the books; they bored me. But this is interesting, Jonathan," George said. "I won't fail at this!"

At noon they were passing through a village. They rested, drank thirstily from the village pump and ate a lunch of bread and cold meat from George's knapsack. From here they could see the arching contour of the mountains, smoke-gray against a cloudless sky. As they went on, the mountains seemed to advance to meet them and to soften in color, deepening to blue, then to the rich purple of a damson plum.

By sunset they were in the foothills. The road narrowed and slanted upward between gray boulders. They located a good camping site on a ledge of rock and George shot a rabbit which he cooked over the embers of the fire Jonathan kindled. As darkness thickened, they threw fresh wood on the fire and sat down beside it.

"Seven o'clock," Jonathan said. "By seven tomorrow night, I'll be having supper at home. And you'll be gadding along toward the Ohio."

"Yes." George stared into the leaping flames. "Jonathan, yesterday you said you have a duty to stay in Caroline County. Perhaps you think there'll be war with England."

26

"Perhaps there will be," Jonathan said. "It seems more than likely. If so, I would volunteer."

"For the colonies? I would, too," George said. "I can't feel that I'm English, or ever was. But you're not thinking that the war would be fought only in the East, are you?"

"Well, the king has soldiers on the coast now," Jonathan answered. "They're in Canada, in Massachusetts and in the southern port cities."

"Yes, but he has troops in the West also, in those towns that France surrendered at the close of the French and Indian War. If the English attack us, they'll seek out our weakest spots—and they'll believe that no spot is as weak as the frontier; they'll bargain with the Indians and use them against us."

"I hadn't thought of that," Jonathan said. "You may be right."

"I *am* right," George declared. "In a war with England, the West would be attacked. And to fight for the West would be *my* duty."

"I see," Jonathan said. "And I wish you luck, George. Whatever your duty is, I know you'll never shirk it."

3

# INDIAN SIGNS

When he had parted from Jonathan, George pushed on toward the Ohio. The land he wanted for his own was one hundred and thirty miles below Pittsburgh, where a creek called Graveyard Run emptied into the river. He reached it in the early autumn. While the weather was still fine he surveyed it, notched the trees at the four corners and sent a small sum of money to Williamsburg, the capital of Virginia, so that the tract could be registered in his name.

Then he could say to himself that it was truly his—this expanse of beautiful forest fronting the placid yellow Ohio!

At first he spent all the daylight hours in hunting and fishing. But as the days shortened, he set about building a shelter for the winter.

He cleared a space in the forest and erected a half-faced camp of three log walls, thatched over with dry branches and brush. The chinks between the logs he plastered with mud and moss. At the open fourth side he dug a shallow pit, in which he kept a fire always blazing, to ward off any prowling animals, as well as to warm him as he slept.

Behind the log shelter he cleared a second space. He had brought a bag of dried corn kernels in his pocket.

Next spring I'll plant a cornfield here, he thought. I'll have all the roasting ears I can eat!

He knew that he had completed his camp none too soon, for now the nights were frosty and a chill wind stripped the trees of foliage. One morning in December he woke to see the world white with snow and a crust of ice at the water's edge. Winter had begun; for months its grasp would be bleak and relentless.

But George had no dread either of winter or of solitude. There was wood for his fire and game for his food. He shot a bear and a panther and cured the skins; they made excellent blankets for his bed of dry leaves and grasses. He trapped beavers and otters on the frozen riverbank and tacked their pelts to his walls to shut out the cold. Sometimes other hunters came through the forest and sat with him by his fire. They told him of other camps, ten miles or so up the creek. Sometimes, with a bundle of beaverskins under his arm, he tramped half a day to the nearest camp, to trade for salt or a sack of flour.

The hunters talked a great deal about the Indians. Iroquois, Cherokee, Shawnee, Delaware and Miami— what a menace they were to the white man! Although George knew that the Indians were cruel, yet he felt a queer sort of sympathy for them.

"They act according to their nature, don't they?" he said to the hunters. "It's not *our* viewpoint, but surely men of any race would hate to see their lands snatched from them. Maybe if we talked the same language we could reason things out and not fight so much."

"Reason? Can you reason with a mad dog? No sirree!" said the hunters. "*You've* got the viewpoint of an east-erner—and you'll find it changes as you go along. Language is nice, but the Indians wear strings of bloody scalps at their waist and *killing* is their nature."

In the spring George sowed his corn and watched the plants sprout up from the fertile soil. He would have a good crop. But he was really not a farmer; and as the forest resumed its bright new green, he wandered out to discover and explore. After that the camp was merely a base of supplies from which he ranged widely up and down the Ohio.

He made a canoe and paddled to the small fort at

Wheeling. There he met Will Harrod and Michael Cresap, two scouts with whom he soon was on terms of friendship. Both men were older than George and far more experienced.

Will Harrod knew Daniel Boone. He told George that Daniel Boone had blazed a trail over the Cumberland Mountains into the bluegrass region of Kentucky.

"Yes, and this summer he's fixin' to bring a big party of settlers from North Carolina over the trail."

"If he can," said Michael Cresap.

"Well, Boone can do it if anyone can," said Harrod.

In the messroom of the dilapidated little fort, George heard more about the movements of the settlers and the Indians, the incessant conflict between them. Will Harrod's brother James was planning to emigrate to the West and build a town in Kentucky—

"If he can," Cresap said again. "Your brother James is a smart fellow, Will, but the tribes are on the rampage. Something's riling them, something's brewing. I see the signs, and I don't relish 'em. The reds are making pilgrimages up to Detroit, big bunches of Iroquois, Miamis, Ouiatenans. They go all that way! And next time you lay eyes on them they've got a stock of mighty pretty guns and ammunition for the guns."

"Detroit?" Harrod said. "It's an army post, headquarters for the British."

"Yes, you bet it is. What I wonder is whether the Indians aren't getting ready for a general attack on us, everywhere—and the British conniving with them."

"That would be bad for poor old Brother Jim," Harrod

31

said. "We'd have to fight then. Stand together and organize, eh? Well, Cresap, you can count on me."

"What about you, Clark?" Cresap asked.

"Yes," George said. "You can count on me, too."

Forty miles above Wheeling was the camp of Logan, chief of the Mingo tribe. Logan was elderly and dignified, and he was not the enemy of white men; he had been named for a white man.

In his wanderings George went to Logan's camp. Logan could speak a little English. He was courteous to George and taught him a little of the Mingo tongue.

Logan was a collector of fine deerskins. He exhibited the collection to George, gave him one of the skins and talked with him about white traders. Some traders had cheated the Mingos, he said, but these were minor offenses and he was not angry. A certain number of white men were dishonest, but they must not all be judged and condemned because of the misconduct of a few. Logan wanted peace and would strive to preserve peace. He could forgive small treacheries, in the hope that he would never suffer a larger one.

A good man, George thought. I like Chief Logan.

In the fall George harvested his corn and sold his crop. He could have sold his forest acres and his shelter, for now more people were coming to claim land on the Ohio. But he said to himself that he would hold on to them—and that he would go home:

"I'll pay the folks a visit and surprise them."

He burst in upon the Clarks as they were having dinner. They were surprised and delighted. They plied him with questions.

32

"Have you been to Kentucky?" Mr. Clark asked.

"No," he said. "But I'm going."

Joseph Rogers was at the plantation that fall, working for Mr. Clark. He was a tall, thin youngster, a nephew of Mrs. Clark's.

Joseph admired his cousin George. "Kentucky? Hey, what a lark," he said. "Let me go with you, George."

"And me!" said Richard.

"And *me!*" shouted William. "Take me to see the Injuns!"

George laughed and picked up William. "How old are you now, William? Three, is it? You've discarded your pinafore and you're looking quite manly. So you want to see the Injuns?"

"William is bolder and more daring every day," said Mrs. Clark.

"He's a little barbarian himself," said Ann, grimacing.

"And more like you, George," said Jonathan.

"*The Injuns!*" roared William.

"Hush," George said. "Hush, you're deafening me! You'll have your chance at the Indians, William—you and Richard both. And, Joe, if you can get your parents' permission I'll take you next time."

Winter was closing in again when George went back to Graveyard Run, and there were tidings of fresh disaster. The settlers whom Daniel Boone was bringing west had been waylaid by Shawnees.

A migratory hunter told George about it.

"Dan'l got his people through the gap in the Cumberland Mountains. That's a deep cleft, crooked as a dog's hind leg, with a path at the bottom. They camped in

Powell's Valley. The Shawnees came at night. In the morning Dan'l had his son Jimmy and five others of his crowd to bury."

George was shocked and sorry. He asked whether Boone had returned to the East.

"Not yet," the hunter said. "He can't—till the weather moderates. But Dan'l is disheartened; and the women and children are plumb scared. Dad-blame those Shawnees! They're tricky as a nest of vipers."

During the winter George thought of Cresap and Will Harrod. He did not hear from them, but he heard more tales of the Indians' brutality.

Settlers were trickling cautiously into the wilderness. They told George that they would keep the Ohio River between their clearings and the Dark and Bloody Ground.

James Harrod, they said, had been routed from Kentucky.

"Jim had fifty men with him. He had wagons, cattle, horses, tools. Jim and his men got forty cabins up and roofed and were commencing on a fort. Harrodsburg, they called the place. Then the Shawnees came and they had to scoot."

"Did the Indians burn Harrod's town?" George asked.

"Nobody knows," the settlers said. "Nobody's been there to see."

George thought conditions seemed to be going from bad to worse. This would be the time for Cresap's organization, the concerted stand of the white men against the marauding reds.

Cresap will be sending for me now, he thought.

As the winter slowly passed, he constantly expected a summons. And in the spring he received it.

At Fort Wheeling Cresap and Will Harrod were marshaling a company to defend the border, and they were counting on George to join them.

So he shouldered his rifle and went to Wheeling.

# FATEFUL MASSACRE

George found that Cresap's company at Wheeling was composed of hunters, traders and trappers, all of them brawny and tough as pine knots. The older men, like Cresap and Will Harrod, were intelligent and sensible, but the younger ones were reckless and wild. They strutted and bragged, cursed and drank to excess. They smeared their faces with paint and danced Indian war dances, howling shrilly and waving their guns.

"They're crazy boys," Will Harrod said to George. "They may do us more harm than good."

George nodded. "Why don't you tone them down, Will?"

"I can't," Harrod said, shrugging. "Cresap's the boss here. It's his job—and between you and me, I think Cresap has bitten off more than he can chew."

George had noticed one big slouching fellow who always flourished a jug as he danced and capered. "Who's that man?" he asked.

"Greathouse, the trader," Harrod answered. "Greathouse sells rum to the Indians."

"I don't like Greathouse's looks," George said. "I wouldn't trust him."

Harrod grunted. "I wouldn't trust any of 'em—much."

Harrod's belief that the "crazy boys" might do more harm than good was justified. Soon it was rumored among them that two white hunters had been scalped on the river road. Without waiting to confirm the rumor, several of Cresap's men rushed out, fell upon a small Shawnee encampment by the river, shot one Indian and imprisoned another.

George knew nothing of the foray until it was over. Then he protested to Harrod. The Shawnees, he said, might have been guilty of the scalping. Then again, they might not. This was not killing in defense of innocent people:

37

"It's killing for the sake of killing, Will. It's what we blame the Indians for—and I'm opposed to it."

"So am I," Harrod said. "Greathouse hatched the scheme. Now the drunken rascal is whispering to his cronies about raiding old Logan."

"*Logan!*" George cried. "Oh, no! Cresap's got to stop that!"

"I wish he would," Harrod said. "You talk to him, Clark."

Cresap was in the fort; George went in at once and talked with him.

"Order the men to keep away from Chief Logan and the Mingos," he said.

Cresap hesitated. "Why should they disturb the Mingos, Clark? I don't figure there's any occasion for the order, but I'll think about it."

While Cresap was thinking, Greathouse was whispering again. Greathouse had a shack on the Ohio near Logan's camp. Two days later Greathouse was at the door of his shack, watching some Mingos, who were fishing from a canoe on the river. Concealed in the woods around the shack were his cronies.

Greathouse shouted to the Indians: "I've got rum for you! Free rum, no trade! Come in, come in!"

The Indians rowed ashore and entered the shack. Greathouse ticked them off on his fingers: eight Mingo braves, a squaw and a baby, and all were relatives of Chief Logan's. When they were seated, Greathouse signaled to his cronies.

In less than an hour the Indians lay dead and horribly

mutilated on the dirt floor; and the white men were wiping the clotted blood from their knives and axes.

The saner members of Cresap's company realized that the massacre would have dire results, and so it did. This was a treachery too enormous for Logan to forgive or ever to forget. The old chief brandished his hatchet and swore he would have ten lives for the life of each of his slaughtered kinsmen. To the chiefs of all the western tribes, he sent messages:

"Crush the white settlers! Comb the forests! Let none escape!"

The chiefs responded and before a month elapsed the feud was raging.

The settlers saw that they were greatly outnumbered and would be overwhelmed. Panic stricken, they gathered up their families and fled for refuge behind the eastern mountains.

In Williamsburg, Lord Dunmore, the royal governor of Virginia, consulted with Daniel Boone. Dunmore was a cold, stern Englishman; he had sternly enforced his king's oppressive laws. He had no love for the king's subjects in Virginia. But he knew that he couldn't allow them to be scalped, tortured, killed by the hundreds—and he was not lacking in courage.

"Boone, these fiends must be repulsed," he said. "Ride the length of the frontier, raise a regiment of militiamen. I'll command them myself."

As Daniel Boone rode the length of the frontier with news of Lord Dunmore's war, men began to come to Wheeling to enlist in the Virginia militia. So many came that the fort had to be enlarged. When the new rooms

39

had been added, the building was renamed Fort Fincastle.

The militiamen elected officers from their ranks—Simon Kenton, Joseph Bowman, Leonard Helm, James Harrod. Cresap, Will Harrod and George Rogers Clark were chosen as the senior captains.

"Of course, Clark's young," the men said. "Not yet twenty-one. But he's all sinew and grit. A plucky, level-headed lad like that, you just can't hold him down!"

During the summer the Indians burned the deserted settlements—and inside Fort Fincastle the Virginians polished and primed their rifles, tested the blades of their long knives.

"Let's have at 'em," they growled. "Let's go!"

"No," said young Captain Clark. "Wait. Lord Dunmore's on the way from Williamsburg with a thousand more recruits. We'll do better fighting one big battle than a lot of skirmishes."

In September Dunmore was at Wheeling. He had left half his regiment on the Kanawha River with Colonel Andrew Lewis, a veteran campaigner.

"Lewis will lead his men up the Kanawha Valley," Dunmore said. "I'll take mine down the Ohio in canoes, our supplies on keelboats. We'll meet Lewis at the junction of the rivers and march on the Shawnees in the Scioto Valley. Boone tells me that Cornstalk, the Shawnee chief, is our most powerful enemy. If we can whip Cornstalk, we'll have little resistance from the other chiefs, and may be able to appease them."

The weather was still warm as the canoes pushed off

from the Wheeling pier. Sunshine gilded the water and
the fine spray from the dipping paddles.

"I don't see any Indians," Bowman said to Captain
Clark, as they glided through the silent country.

"They must be playing 'possum somewhere," George
said.

Lord Dunmore's small fleet beached at the junction of
the rivers; but Colonel Andrew Lewis was not there.
Dunmore camped for the night. Next morning a runner
brought him a report: a battle had been fought at Point
Pleasant—and Lewis was wounded.

"It was the Shawnees, sir," the runner said. "Cornstalk
must have had spies out; he must have known it was the
time to blast at us, before you got here. Six hundred
Shawnees forded the Kanawha in the dark, crawled up
around us and attacked at dawn. All day they pounded,
and they seemed to be winning; we thought we were
done for. Toward evening, Colonel Lewis took the offensive, then Cornstalk fell back, the Shawnees recrossed
the river—"

"And Lewis followed them?" asked Dunmore, inter-
rupting.

"No, sir. He couldn't, he had a bullet through his leg.
And it was night again and we were plumb tuckered out.
Anyway, we knew that once they got us in the forest
we'd be ambushed. Six officers and forty of our men were
killed, and many wounded."

Dunmore looked grim. "What about the dead and
wounded Shawnees?"

"Well, they lost even more, sir. Oh, it was an ugly
thing!" The runner shuddered. "Blood everywhere."

"Ugly, yes, but the final effect may be good," Dunmore said. "Cornstalk is not a fool. I think he's telling himself right now that if he couldn't defeat half my army, it would be absurd to attack both halves. While Lewis is nursing his injuries at Point Pleasant, I'll go on into the Shawnee territory."

Dunmore marched into the Scioto Valley, and he was not challenged until he reached the big Indian village at Chillicothe. There Cornstalk and several other chieftains barred his path. But the Indians were not armed; they had come to ask for a truce.

"They want me to confer with them at Camp Charlotte," Dunmore said. "I'll oblige them, for I'm curious to hear whether Cornstalk has learned his lesson. Captain Clark, you may attend the powwow with me. And you, too, Captain Bowman."

Cornstalk was the spokesman for the chiefs at Camp Charlotte. The tribes, he said, would return the prisoners they had taken from Colonel Lewis and would cease their raiding of the settlements south of the Ohio River if Lord Dunmore would stop his war against them.

Lord Dunmore thought over these terms and then accepted them. When Cornstalk handed him a lighted peace pipe, he smoked it solemnly.

George looked around for Chief Logan at the conference, but did not see him.

"Logan didn't come," Dunmore said. "He sent a letter. Logan can't write; he dictated his letter and somebody else wrote it down. I shall read it aloud to my army. Logan seems to believe that the massacre was entirely Michael Cresap's fault."

George shook his head. "It wasn't, sir. Not entirely. I think Cresap might have prevented it. At least he should have disciplined the troops at Wheeling more strictly. But perhaps we were all somewhat at fault."

Logan's letter was brief. George listened sorrowfully as Lord Dunmore read it:

I appeal to any white man to say if he ever entered Logan's cabin hungry, and he gave him not meat; if ever he came cold and naked and he clothed him not. During the last long and bloody war, Logan remained quiet in his cabin, an advocate of peace. Such was my love for the whites that my countrymen, as they passed, said, 'Logan is the friend of white men.' I had even thought to live with you, but for the injuries of one man, Colonel Cresap, who the last spring, in cold blood and unprovoked, murdered all the relations of Logan, not sparing even my women and children. There runs not a drop of my blood in the veins of any living creature. This called on me for revenge. I have sought it; I have killed many; I have fully glutted my vengeance. For my country, I rejoice at the beams of peace. But do not harbor a thought that mine is the joy of fear. Logan never felt fear. He will not turn on his heel to save his life. Who is there to mourn for Logan? Not one.

# 5

## POWDER FOR PIONEERS

In 1774 many people were acquiring land south of the
Ohio. Lord Dunmore's powwow with the chiefs at Camp
Charlotte had opened the way for settlers. Those earliest
pioneers, who had been frightened out by the Indians'

uprising, flocked back again. James Harrod, with a new batch of homesteaders, rebuilt his town—the first permanent settlement in Kentucky, though within a few months three more towns would be established there.

For years George had wanted to see Kentucky; and after Dunmore's war he crossed the river and explored the vast green country.

"You could not imagine a lovelier place," he wrote to his brother Jonathan. "The land is rich and may be had very cheaply. I'll get some for myself and some for Father."

George was employed to survey the new claims. His services were much in demand; he traveled from job to job, making friends wherever he went.

"You seem to know all the squatters in the bluegrass, Clark," James Harrod said to him once, when he was in Harrodsburg.

"I guess I do know most of them," George said.

Harrod grinned. "And they all like you."

"Well, that's good."

"You're a redheaded young giant with brains and spunk. These folks feel that you'll stick to them through thick and thin. And they're pretty nervous about the Indians, Clark," James Harrod said. "Things are quiet, but we mustn't think the savages are licked for keeps. They may hit us again."

"Yes," George said. "We've got to watch them."

"And if they hit us, what can we do?"

George looked thoughtful and said, "I wonder. It's a problem, Jim."

45

The problem was often in George's mind—and there was another matter, quite as perplexing.

Who really had the right to this fertile region? To whom did Kentucky actually belong?

The royal governors of Virginia had contended that it was a part of the original Virginia colony; settlers on the land had believed that they were Virginians. But colonists in Pennsylvania said that sections of it belonged to them. Spain claimed it because of Spanish explorations a century ago. From time to time different groups of English investors had bought large overlapping tracts from the Iroquois tribes.

Now in 1775 more claimants were appearing. Richard Henderson, a wealthy and ambitious businessman, was in Kentucky. Henderson was the agent for some investors who called themselves the Transylvania Company. He said that he had obtained all the territory between the Kentucky and the Cumberland rivers, every mile of it, from the Cherokees. The land would be divided and sold, Henderson said. Any persons who at present were occupying it would either have to move or to pay him for their farms and homesteads.

Daniel Boone had been working with Henderson. At Henderson's request, Boone had arranged for a meeting of the Cherokees on the Holston River. Twelve hundred Cherokees went to the meeting. Henderson distributed among them lavish gifts of beads and cloth, muskets and metal cooking utensils, glassware, jewelry and china dishes.

Henderson told the Indians that these shiny articles were worth thousands of dollars. He did not say that the land he bargained for was worth a million times as much —or that it might not be the property of the Indians to sell.

The Cherokees were dazzled. They hastened to scratch their marks on contracts which they were unable to read. Then Henderson commissioned Daniel Boone to build a road through the Cumberland Gap into the new domain of Transylvania.

Daniel Boone was a scout, not a businessman. He built the road—the famous Wilderness Road, which would endure forever. He never suspected that Henderson's scheme was fraudulent or that the Indians had been badly cheated.

But George Rogers Clark was shrewder.

Kentucky is not Transylvania, George thought. "It's not to be bought or sold or traded by any dishonest man or group of men who takes a fancy to it. Kentucky *is* a part of Virginia. Perhaps the solution of the problem would be to make it a *separate part*, a county, with its own government."

Meanwhile in the East the thirteen American colonies had united and had held their Continental Congress to prepare for a war of rebellion against the English king. The faint rumblings of great events gradually sifted out to the frontier.

"In a year, or maybe only a few months, every man in America will have to decide whether to be loyal to the king or to the colonists' cause," George said to James Harrod.

"Well, there's no doubt which side we're on," Harrod

47

said. "We're Americans, ain't we? We'll fight to protect our homes."

"Yes, but we ought to know that the homes *are* ours. We need a government here, Jim."

Harrod shifted the wad of tobacco in his cheek and nodded. "What we need most is ammunition. We've got no powder for our guns and no cash to swap for it. The fact is, Clark, if the tribes kicked up a fuss now, we'd be smashed to smithereens."

"I think we'll have to ask the Virginia legislature for help," George said. "Suppose you call our people together, Jim. We'll vote on it."

One hot June day in 1776 the Kentuckians congregated in Harrodsburg and voted to appeal to the Virginia House of Burgesses for a separate government and a stock of gunpowder. Two men were delegated to represent them at Williamsburg—George Rogers Clark and John Gabriel Jones.

That was a very wet summer in the West. The delegates rode over trails deep in mud. Their horses floundered and stumbled; on the third day Jones's horse sank exhausted in the mire.

"Reckon we ought to shoot the beast, put him out of his misery," Gabriel Jones said.

"Oh, no," George protested. "We can haul him up and leave him on solid ground. When he's rested, he'll find his way back."

"And I'll ride double with you, eh?" Jones said, as they dragged the fallen horse up from the sinkhole.

"No, you take my horse. I'll walk."

"Walk!" Jones was sweating and puffing. "Seven hundred miles!"

"Why not?" George said. "My legs are long and I've done it before."

So for days and weeks he walked through the hot, steamy forest beside the plodding horse. Jones had an old map which showed three villages on the trail.

"We can sleep in the villages," Jones said. "I like to sleep with a roof above me."

But the villages existed only on the map now; the Indians had burned them.

Jones looked at the heaps of blackened ashes. "Varmints!" he exclaimed. "If we could just rid this country of the red varmints!"

"Or learn to live peaceably with them," George said.

Jones sniffed and jerked the horse to a trot. "I don't hanker for Indians, myself."

George smiled and lengthened his stride. He could not have defined his feeling about the Indians, but he was rather sure red men had often been mistreated.

At last the travelers emerged from the forest to a good road which took them into a town. That night they spent in a tavern. As they ate supper in the tavern's candlelit taproom, they heard the talk of other travelers—and were startled by it.

Tremendous changes had occurred in America recently, changes of which the Kentuckians knew nothing.

The war with England had become a reality. In the northwestern colonies, in Canada, in the South—yes, even on the coast of Virginia—the Americans had engaged British troops in battle, and sometimes rebuffed them.

George Washington of Virginia was commanding the colonies' combined forces; France and Spain were sending money and military supplies to Washington's army. Thomas Jefferson of Virginia had written America's Declaration of Independence; the Continental Congress had approved the splendid document; one by one the thirteen colonies were ratifying it.

Breathless with amazement, the delegates from Harrodsburg listened.

"What about Governor Dunmore?" George inquired.

"Dunmore? Oh, he's not our governor now," said the tavern guests. "Dunmore was deposed, chased out of Williamsburg by the Minute Men of Hanover County. That's Patrick Henry's county. He's a great man, Patrick Henry, a true patriot! Our new House of Burgesses made him governor of Virginia in Dunmore's stead."

"Is Governor Henry in Williamsburg now?"

"No, and he won't be there till fall, when the legislature convenes again. Henry's at his plantation in Hanover."

"Thank you, gentlemen," George said. "Thank you for the information."

Later, in their bedroom, Jones said gloomily that the trip had been fruitless.

"We can't stay in Williamsburg all summer, Clark."

"No, but we could go to Hanover," George said.

"To see Governor Henry? He'd have too much to do to bother with the likes of us!"

George thought about the tavern guests' description of Patrick Henry. A great man? A patriot?

"He might be willing to bother with us, Jones."

50

Jones flung himself down on the bed. "Well, I'm not going to Hanover."

"I am," George said. "This war is a revolution. The American Revolution. Our Kentucky people will need ammunition now more than ever. I'm going to get it for them."

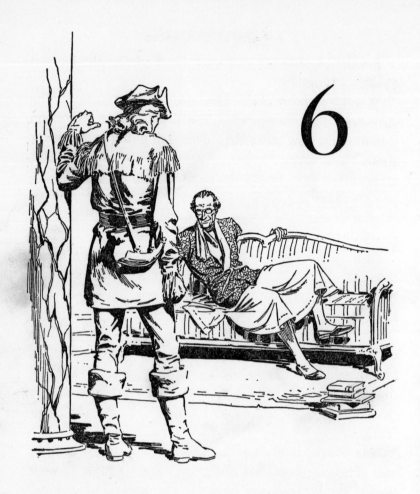

6

## A PLEA FOR HELP

The Negro servant at the door of the house in Hanover said that Governor Henry was ill. He peered at the tall young man on the veranda, at his shaggy red hair and travel-stained clothing.

"Is the governor expecting you, sir?"

"No, but I've come seven hundred miles to see him."

"Your name, sir?"

"George Rogers Clark. I'm from Kentucky."

"Step in, sir," the servant said. "Please wait a moment."

George waited anxiously. He had more information about Patrick Henry now. This man was a lawyer and an orator, a fiery champion of the colonists' cause. At a revolutionary convention in Virginia he had shouted in ringing, resounding tones: "Give me liberty or give me death!"

He'll understand what I'm trying to do, George thought.

The servant reappeared and beckoned. "In the library, sir."

Patrick Henry was lying on a couch. He was a man of forty, big and rawboned, with piercing black eyes, a long nose, a firm mouth and chin. He wore a dark silk dressing gown with a white muslin scarf around his throat and a light wool shawl thrown over his slippered feet.

"Mr. Clark? Sit down," he said, and his voice was firm, too. "Have a chair. Ah, the chairs are all stacked with books. Well, brush the books to the floor. There, now! Are you comfortable? You look tired. I'll have biscuits and a glass of wine fetched for you. I know your name. The Clarks of Caroline County. An old family. One of your brothers, Jonathan, is the captain of a company of our Virginia volunteers."

"Jonathan? Is he?" George smiled. "I hadn't heard that."

53

Governor Henry nodded. "You've been in the back-woods. And why are you here?"

"I want your advice, sir—and your help."

"In what regard?" Henry waved his hand to the serv-ant who was entering with a tray. "Put the tray on that table. Some wine, Mr. Clark. Your health, sir! And mine, for I'm ailing. Now then, something is vexing you. Tell me—and take your time about it. The whole story."

George sipped the wine. He was warmed by it and by the governor's hospitality. He told his story, how Kentuckians were so confused about the ownership of their farms, how constantly they were threatened by the Indians.

"We want to be a separate county of Virginia," he explained, "and we must have powder for our guns."

"The business of making a separate county would be a transaction for the legislature," Henry said. "The legis-lature is not in session."

"Yes, sir, I know."

"But the powder—sorely needed, is it? Well, Mr. Clark, we must get it for you, if possible! Fetch me paper and my pen from the desk yonder. The executive council of Virginia is in Williamsburg. I shall write a letter to the council, urging that the powder be granted to you im-mediately. How much, sir? Five hundred pounds? It is not a great deal, but we do not have a large stock, and our troops are using it up fast, peppering the scarlet coats of the king's soldiers."

"I'll be grateful for five hundred pounds," George said.

The Governor wrote rapidly. "I'm advising that it be sent to Pittsburgh. I suppose you can take it from there down the Ohio—on a flatboat. But you can't do that alone, eh?"

"No, I'll get some of our Kentuckians to come and make the voyage with me." George folded the letter and put it into his pocket. "You're very kind, Governor."

"We are partners in a lofty enterprise, Mr. Clark," Patrick Henry said. "You and I have the same goal—which is freedom for all Americans. Good day, sir. And my compliments!"

The gentlemen of the executive council were not as impulsive as the governor of Virginia. Indeed, George had never encountered men who seemed so slow thinking and deliberate. They read the governor's letter, then stared questioningly at George.

A grant of powder for the frontier? Was it lawful?

"Will you guarantee to pay for the powder, Mr. Clark, if it should be seized by the British on the way?"

No, George could not guarantee that. He had a few dollars in his purse—pitifully few!—and no funds in reserve.

"Will you pay the expense of transportation?"

"Gentlemen, I cannot. But there shouldn't be much expense. If the powder is delivered to me at Pittsburgh, I'll hire a flatboat and see that it reaches Kentucky."

For almost a month the council debated, while George lingered in Williamsburg, fretfully pacing the streets, wondering about his friends in the remote forest clearings, whether they were still unmolested—or even still alive. The war was spreading. The British were luring Indians into their ranks as allies.

Has there been fighting in the wilderness? he wondered.

Late in August he was notified that at Governor Henry's insistence the council was sending five hundred pounds of gunpowder to the dock at Pittsburgh. He dispatched a message to James Harrod:

> I want a convoy of reliable boatmen, Jim. Start them east at once, and let me know when they leave. I'll be waiting for your reply. Then I'll meet the men in Pittsburgh.

It would be a week or two before he could hear from Harrod. He decided to go home to Caroline County for that length of time. Jonathan would not be there.

But the others will be—and happy to see me, he thought.

The reunion with his parents, his sisters and brothers was all he could have wished for. He tramped over the plantation with his father and young Richard, played with the little children, lounged at ease in the parlor and was feasted, petted and praised.

Ann was married now; she was Mrs. Owen Gwathmey.

"So you finally caught a husband, did you?" George teased. "Where is he, Ann?"

"In the Army," she said. "Everybody's in the Army."

"George, are you a soldier?" William asked.

"I have been. And will be again, probably."

"Jonathan's a soldier," William said. "He has the nicest uniform."

"Hurrah for Jonathan! I've never had a uniform,

William. Out west we went to war in the rags we had on our backs."

"You look fine to me, George," Richard asserted, leaning against him.

"Yes, George," William said, climbing into his lap, "you're nice, anyway."

Joseph Rogers came over one day from his father's farm.

"Hey, George, you told me I could go to Kentucky with you next time, if my folks didn't mind," Joe said. "Well, it *is* next time—and they don't."

George had forgotten. "I shouldn't have told you that, Joe. You're just a boy."

Joe straightened to his full height. "I'm a man. I'm older than you were when you first went out there."

"Yes, but you wouldn't be going on a lark, Joe. The West is a wild, rugged place."

"I could stand it," Joe said. "If you don't take me, I'll sign with Jonathan's outfit. Ann is right. Every able-bodied man is doing *something* useful now. And I won't be the exception."

George was silent, then he sighed. He knew how his young cousin felt. "In a couple of weeks I'll be shoving off from Fort Pitt," he said. "If you're at the dock that morning, you can board my flatboat."

"I'll be at the dock," Joe said.

The two weeks passed and James Harrod had not replied. George was in Williamsburg again, waiting—a month, two months.

What was the matter with Harrod? Why didn't he write?

In the autumn the Virginia legislature convened. The burgesses arrived in the capital, their carriages crowding the sandy, tree-bordered streets. George thought wearily of the precious days he was wasting. How could he put them to some advantage?

An idea came to him. He began to speak to the members of the legislature, introducing himself and telling them about the plight of Kentucky. He stopped them as they strolled on Duke of Gloucester Street, or on the green of William and Mary College, or in the taverns. He went into the halls of the Capitol and addressed them as they sat in session.

"You believe, don't you, that Kentucky is a part of Virginia, and not the private property of Richard Henderson and his associates?" he said. "You know that most of the Kentuckians were born and bred here in Virginia —and merit your friendship? You have favored us with a parcel of ammunition—but that is not all we should have from your legislature. You must grant us the privilege of becoming a new county of Virginia, so that we can make our own laws and raise a militia for our defense."

The weeks passed, but he persisted. The burgesses said to each other that this young Clark was obstinate— as obstinate as a mule. But he seemed to know what he was talking about, and he seemed to have Governor Henry's esteem. And, really, why shouldn't the Kentuckians have their own government? What was the objection to it?

In December, by vote of the legislators, Kentucky was

made a county of Virginia—which might soon be a free American state.

George was elated. But still he hadn't heard from James Harrod. He thought that Harrod must not have received his message. Well, he would simply have to get the powder to Harrodsburg without a convoy, as best he could!

It was winter and the weather was freezing cold. Buttoning his coat to his chin and fastening the flaps of his fur cap over his ears, he left Williamsburg and walked through the bleak country to Pittsburgh.

He knew that the kegs of powder would be in a warehouse at the dock. He went directly to the warehouse, and there was Joseph Rogers.

"George!" cried Joe. "Where on earth have you been?"

"I was detained, Joe. I'm sorry it was so long."

"Oh, I didn't mind too much," Joe said. "I've been working for a blacksmith in the town. But I was always looking for you."

George was examining the kegs. "Has anyone else looked for me? Any fellows from the West?"

"Yes," Joe said. "A man named Jones. He's at the fort. John Gabriel Jones. Here, I brought you this."

George took the little leather pouch which Joseph was offering him. He shook the pouch. "What's in it? Coins?"

"Silver. From your father. He said it might come in handy."

George grinned. "It will! I haven't a penny. Good for Father! And you say Jones is at the fort? Let's go and find him."

59

They found Jones in the messroom of the fort. He was eating his dinner.

"Hello, Clark," he said. "So you've turned up? I reckoned you would. I didn't go back to Kentucky. I've been in and around Pittsburgh all summer. I'll go back with you. When do you start?"

"Now," George said.

"This afternoon? The British have had spies at the dock."

George squared his shoulders. "Come on, Jones. You hire a boat for me and I'll get a crew."

# PERILOUS VOYAGE

George quickly got his crew from among the many inhabitants of Pittsburgh who earned their living on the river. Six men would be enough, he thought. He paid them with the silver from the leather pouch and rushed

61

them to the dock, where Jones and Joe Rogers were stamping up and down, excited and shivering.

Jones had the boat moored to the pier. It was a flat-boat, small and old, but solid, with a low-roofed cabin and a full set of poles.

"We can stow the powder in the cabin," George said. "We'd better hurry, the temperature's dropping and it's beginning to snow."

Jones had seen a canoe packed with Indians paddling away from the dock. "They went downstream just an hour ago," he said. "Maybe they're in cahoots with the British. Maybe they mean to stop in some convenient cove, intercept us and steal our cargo."

"We'll keep behind them," George said. "The snow will screen us. Tonight, when it's good and dark, we'll slip past them."

The crew carried the powder from the warehouse, stooping under the weight of the powder kegs. George superintended the loading so that the boat would be evenly balanced. Jones and Joe Rogers set the poles into position. The sky was gray, the snow moist and clinging.

At three o'clock they shoved off and poled out into the current. George took his place at the front of the boat, wielding the long broad sweep which would direct the course. Jones had the rear sweep, while the other men were at the side poles. There was a little brick fire-place in the cabin, with a chimney above; but George said no fire would be kindled in it.

"The smoke might be seen," he said. "And we won't have a lantern, either. The less light, the better."

The river was high, the current swift and tumbling.

The swirling snow curtained the boat so closely that the shores were scarcely visible. Alert and silent, the men guided the cumbersome craft through the churning water, while the wet snowflakes coated their garments and gave them the look of bulky white statues.

Dusk came early. Just as the sky darkened into night, at a bend in the river, an arrow whizzed from the shadows, grazed the cabin chimney and splashed in the water beyond.

"George!" Joe Rogers shouted. "George, that missed you by an inch—"

"Hush, Joe!" George warned. "Pull, boys! Pull like fury!"

They pulled and half an hour later Elkin, the biggest and burliest of the boatmen said, "Reckon we're safe now?"

"We'll be safe when we're at Harrodsburg," George answered tersely, "and not before."

The night was black and long, but quiet. The snow thinned and ceased completely. The boat forged ahead. Then, shortly after dawn, Jones shouted that he had seen a canoe glide out from a willow thicket to midstream.

"It's following us! Indians. Mingos! They have guns!"

George glanced back at the canoe. Yes, it was certainly following. He could see its occupants, bending to the paddles; they were certainly Indians.

"Well, boys," he said calmly, "it's a race. Let's beat the rascals."

But he did not feel calm, for he knew it was a race he must not lose. The flatboat was clumsy, the canoe graceful and speedy. There was only one slim chance of escape

—and he took it. They were at the mouth of a small creek. He swerved the boat abruptly into the inlet.

"Tie up to the bank," he said to the men. "This is Limestone Creek. There are three caves in the bank. I've seen them. We'll roll the powder kegs off and hide them in the caves."

Toiling frantically, the men rolled the kegs up the incline and into the caves. They dragged brush over the openings. At George's command, they sprang back to the boat deck, grasped their poles and swung away, out of the creek and into the river.

The canoe was now within rifle range. Jones lifted his gun.

"No!" George shouted. "We've got to keep going and draw them off the scent!"

They kept going until they reached a projecting point of land. There they grounded the flatboat, jumped out and waded ashore. As they scrambled through the dense undergrowth, they heard the Indians' yells of triumph. The Indians had seized the flatboat.

"And let them have it!" George muttered. "It's not the prize they think it is!"

But he was thinking of the gunpowder. Not for a moment had he relinquished his intention of delivering it to his friends in Kentucky!

He calculated the distance to Harrodsburg as being about ninety miles.

"We can cut through the woods. There's a buffalo trace," he told the men. "At Harrodsburg, we'll get a party to come and move the powder."

They found the trace and all day they walked through

the forest. In the evening they saw an empty log hut and crawled inside to sleep.

But George was too worried to sleep soundly, and at daybreak a crackling of twigs and the soft pad-pad of moccasins roused him. He crept to the door. He saw a man approaching—was it Simon Kenton of Harrodsburg?

"Kenton?" he called softly.

"Clark!"

Then they clasped hands, and both said: "What are *you* doing here?"

Kenton, with two companions, had been on a hunting trip. The hunters had killed a deer. Kenton went back to their camp near the buffalo trace and brought his companions to the log hut.

"You know what day this is?" Kenton said. "December twenty-fourth. Christmas Eve. We'll skin the deer and broil some thick steaks of venison; we'll have a banquet."

Kenton had seen other hunters on the trace. He suggested that they get these men to assist them in taking the ammunition on to Harrodsburg, but George thought a larger party would be needed.

"No," he said. "You and I will go on to the town and get help, Kenton. Jones can round up the other hunters and stay here with them. Then we'll all fetch the powder from the caves. That way, we'll be strong enough to fight off the Mingos if they sneak up on us."

When they had eaten the venison steaks, George and Simon Kenton started forward. They walked fast, for they were accustomed to the forest paths. At midnight they were in Harrodsburg, knocking on the door of James Harrod's cabin.

Harrod opened the door and shone a candle on them.

"It's me, Jim," George said. "Clark—and Kenton."

"Clark!" Harrod stared. "You're a sight for sore eyes. I thought something had happened to you in the East."

"No. I sent you a message—"

"I didn't get it."

"But I did send it. It must have gone astray."

But this was not the time for wondering about the message. George plunged into his story of the powder secreted on Limestone Creek. He said that men must be hastened to the spot where Jones had been left with Kenton's hunters and the crew of the flatboat.

"I'll go myself," Harrod said. "I'll take my brother Will and Leonard Helm. We'll fetch those kegs, Clark. You and Kenton sleep now till morning. You're plumb fagged out."

George lay down on a cot and slept—and was wakened by the touch of Harrod's hand on his shoulder. He sat up. Gray daylight suffused the cabin. He blinked and remembered suddenly that this was Christmas Day.

"Clark, somebody's here," Harrod said. "A fellow named Elkin."

Elkin was standing on the hearth. He was haggard, his cheeks and chin were streaked with blood.

"I've got news, Clark, and it's bad."

Elkin wiped blood from his face and told his news haltingly.

Jones had thought he was capable of moving the powder from the caves to Harrodsburg without reinforcements. Jones had led the hunters and the crew of the flatboat several miles along the buffalo trace—right into a nest of Mingo warriors. Jones and three of the men had been shot to death, three were taken prisoner.

"The rest of us got loose," Elkin said. "The Mingos crossed the river and went north."

"Was young Rogers killed?" George asked.

"No, captured. And the Mingos didn't smell out the kegs. They're still where we hid 'em."

George stamped into his boots, buckled on his knife and picked up his rifle. He felt heartsick, knowing that Joe Rogers was a captive of the Mingos. But he had a task to finish.

"Ready, Harrod?" he said. "We'll fetch the gunpowder."

8

## A HAZARDOUS BUSINESS

Soon after New Year's Day the twenty kegs of gunpowder were stacked in the Harrodsburg blockhouse. "Clark got 'em for us," said the people of the settlement, as they peered in at the kegs. "Young Clark—and nobody else could have done it! If we're to organize our own militia, Clark's the man to do that, too."

So early in 1777 George became Major Clark, commanding the militia of the newly formed county of Kentucky. Rugged as an oak tree, but just twenty-four, he found himself responsible for the lives and safety of his neighbors.

Making the rounds of the stations, from Harrodsburg to McClellan's Fort, from Boonesborough to St. Asaph's, George thought often of Joe Rogers.

Poor Joe! he thought. Where is he? If only I could have saved Joe!

He saw that the Indians were raiding again. Cattle had been stolen, workers shot down in the grain fields, and the fields burned over, white hunters scalped in the forests. The settlers were tense and frightened. Though they used the precious gunpowder sparingly, the supply was dwindling. At night the weird, taunting cries of the savages sounded beyond their log stockades. By moonlight dark figures skulked and wailed outside their fences.

George was convinced that the British constantly sent weapons and ammunition to the Indians.

"The British are bribing the tribes to nag at us," he told James Harrod.

"Yes, I reckon so," Harrod agreed. "Reckon Lord Dunmore smoked that peace pipe in vain at Camp Charlotte."

"Well, the whole situation is different, Jim," George said. "Dunmore is our enemy now. He's against us. Dunmore and his henchmen are influencing the Indians to fight us. The British have an army at Detroit. The officer in charge is Colonel Hamilton; he is cunning and ruth-less. There are British military posts in Illinois, at Kas-kaskia and Cahokia, and one at the French town of Vincennes on the Wabash River. If Hamilton should sweep down from Detroit, he could conquer the West in three months' time."

"And then would he march east?" Harrod asked.

"Of course! With a big army of Indians."

Harrod whistled between his teeth. "That would be the end of the Revolution, wouldn't it?"

"Yes. And a sorry end for Americans."

"You say the situation is different, Clark—is it hope-less? Are we lost?"

George answered slowly: "Maybe not . . . maybe not."

When Harrod left him, he stood at the door of the log hut which was his headquarters. It was spring; the trees were green. Planting time—but no crops had been sowed in the settlers' clearings. What was the good of planting corn if it could never be harvested? The squares of pasture ought to be thick-grown with grass at this season, but fires had withered them. The one cow which had survived the Indians' thieving was penned into the confines of the stockade, where it ambled dolefully about, tinkling the bell tied at its scrawny neck. The people in the forty cabins were on scant rations now; next winter they would be starving. And there were more women and children to suffer the pangs of hunger, for the men were the special targets for the savages' arrows and bullets.

George stepped out of his hut and knocked on the door of Joseph Bowman's cabin.

"Bowman," he said, "for days I've been thinking of a plan. It's a rash plan, perhaps too rash ever to be put into operation, but it has tormented me. I'd like to tell you about it. Come over. Bring Ben Linn, Will Harrod and Leonard Helm. Yes, and Sam Moore. Nobody else is to know."

Bowman smiled and saluted. "We'll come, Major."

The men sat at George's table, with the May sunshine shafting in—and fading as the hours went by. George explained his plan, and somehow as he talked he saw it as a definite and detailed pattern.

He meant to make an expedition to the British forts in Illinois and on the Wabash, to seize them and hold them henceforth in the name of the Continental Congress. In this way, Hamilton's descent upon the western country might be prevented.

"If I can bring it off, the American forces everywhere will be strengthened and our people in Kentucky will get instant relief from the terror in which they're living now," he said. "The Indians will let us alone and we can be safe—and prosper."

The men murmured and looked dubious.

"How would you go about such an expedition?" Bowman asked. "How would you start it?"

George had thought of that. He would start by sending spies to Kaskaskia, Cahokia and Vincennes.

"The spies would get a full report on the forts we propose to attack. The size of the garrisons in the forts, the number of guns and cannon in each one, the ammunition on hand, and the feeling of the inhabitants of the towns. They are French. My father once said to me that those

71

French people have never liked knuckling under to the British. If that is so, if they resent the British soldiers quartered on them, they may rally to us. We can't be sure of it—but it's a possibility."

"And when you have the reports, what then?"

"The next thing would be to get Governor Henry's endorsement."

"Can you get Henry's endorsement?" Will Harrod asked.

"I don't know, Will," George said. "But I can go to Williamsburg and find out."

Ben Linn was fidgeting impatiently on his bench. He was a small, bright-eyed youth of twenty, agile and tawny as a fox.

"I could spy for you, Major," Ben said. "I'd like to. It'd be just my dish."

"A dangerous dish, Ben."

"Oh, I don't care. I've roamed over most of Illinois, hither and yon. I'd pose as a hunter, drift into the Frenchies' towns, listen to their gossip and tittle-tattle, drift out again—and none of 'em the wiser."

"And if the Britishers caught you?"

"They couldn't do more than hang me, could they, Major?"

George smiled. "Thanks, Ben, but I think we ought to have two spies. We'll draw lots for it. What do you say, boys? Isn't that fair?"

They all said it was fair; then Ben darted through the door to pluck six poplar twigs for the drawing. Soon he was back, the twigs grasped in his brown fist.

"The two shortest ones, Major," Ben said.

"Very well," George assented. "Let's draw. And don't forget, any of you, that this is a secret."

They drew and then compared the twigs.

"Mine's short!" Will Harrod exclaimed.

"And mine's shorter," said Sam Moore. "But thunderation—you can't hardly see the one Ben got. Why, it's a litty-bitty thing—"

"Shortest in the bunch," Ben said, winking. "Ain't you surprised? 'Specially since I plucked 'em?"

Linn and Moore slipped away from Harrodsburg one warm night when the candle in Major Clark's hut was the only flicker of light in the clearing. They had kept their secret. Even their families believed they were off for an ordinary hunting excursion.

As the gate of the stockade shut silently behind the departing spies, George and Captain Bowman were bending over a piece of paper spread on the table before them. Written on the paper was a list of names, the roster of the Kentucky militia.

George studied the list and sighed. "Mighty few names, Bowman!"

"Yes." Bowman made an X with his quill pen. "This one is out. The fellow's dead, scalped just yesterday. He had a wife and two babies."

"And who's to take his place, eh? Bowman, we've got to have men. I want you to scour the county for them."

"There are mighty few to find, Major."

"Oh, I know. But beat the bushes, uncover them, dig them up!"

"I'll do my best."

"Bowman," George said—and paused, frowning.

73

"Yes, Major Clark?"

"You have a cool head," George said earnestly. "I value your opinion. Tell me, am I mad to trust this plan?"

"You're not mad," Bowman answered. "Never that, my friend. But it is a hazardous business."

# ORDERS -- AND "FORWARD ALL!"

On a sparkling, crisp December morning Major Clark
of the Kentucky militia rode into Williamsburg. Dis-
mounting in front of the Raleigh Tavern, he handed the

reins of his mud-splashed horse to the Negro groom at the curbstone.

" 'Pears like you've come a long way, sir," the groom said.

George smiled. "Yes, and every mile of it was familiar to me. Here's a coin. See that my horse is fed, will you? The poor thing is famished."

As the groom took the horse to the stables, George glanced up and down the street. Duke of Gloucester Street it was. And how neat it looked, the fine brick dwellings hemmed in by clipped hedges, the shops with scrubbed doorsills and glass-paned windows. Tidy freshly painted carriages were passing, driven by liveried coachmen. The pedestrians were well clad, the men in cockaded hats and greatcoats, the ladies in frilled bonnets and capes of fur or homespun.

"And how shabby I am!" George said to himself. "I must fix up a bit before I call on the governor."

He went into the tavern taproom for a breakfast of ham and eggs. As he ate, he read a copy of the *Virginia Gazette*. The war news was interesting.

He read that the British were in Philadelphia and General Washington had encamped for the winter at Valley Forge. In New York there had been much fighting; American troops had crushed the British regiments of General Burgoyne in a series of assaults. Turning a page, he read that the Continental Congress had adopted the Articles of Confederation, a measure by which the colonies became a union of states. The banner of the Union would be the Stars and Stripes; thirteen stripes of red and white and thirteen white stars on a blue field.

Very beautiful, George thought. I'd like to see the Stars and Stripes.

After breakfast he went to the tailor's shop where he purchased two ruffled linen shirts, a velveteen jacket and a pair of polished boots. But he did not call on the governor that day, for he had some writing to do. In a small notebook he recorded the information which Ben Linn and Samuel Moore had collected for him on their tour of Illinois, and the names of those few recruits whom Captain Bowman had recently added to the Kentucky militia roster.

Leafing through his notebook, he thought of the plan he would soon disclose to Governor Henry. What would the governor say about it? Was it indeed, as Bowman had remarked, a hazardous business?

He slept with the notebook under his pillow. Early next morning he donned his new garments and, feeling quite respectable, went to the governor's office.

Patrick Henry was cordial. He waved George to a chair and lighted his pipe.

"Well, young man, since our conversation of a year ago, you have become Major Clark, eh?" he said. "You are here to tell me about the Indian atrocities in Kentucky and what might be done to remedy them?"

"Yes, sir," George said. "I've had spies out. My spies have confirmed the suspicion that the British at Detroit are the source of all our troubles. Colonel Hamilton is known as the Hair Buyer. He pays in gold for every American scalp brought in to him. When the time is ripe, Hamilton will come down and complete our ruin. In this

77

notebook I have sketched a campaign which might possibly stop Hamilton."

Governor Henry looked at George's notebook. "Why, it's a conquest of enemy posts in Illinois, itemized step by step!"

"Yes. My theory is that we ought not to wait to be destroyed. We should attack—and while the British garrisons are napping. I want your endorsement, sir, and your support."

"My support?" Governor Henry arched his dark eyebrows.

"I wish I were not obliged to ask the state of Virginia for men and money," George said. "But the people of Kentucky are destitute."

"Men and money? Both commodities are at a premium here as elsewhere, Major Clark. I don't know what support Virginia could provide. But your idea is a brilliant one," Patrick Henry said, and his eyes flashed. "Brilliant! Let me talk it over with some of my friends. Come back in a fortnight."

When George went back again to the Capitol, Thomas Jefferson, George Wythe and George Mason were seated with the governor. These men were members of the House of Burgesses. Like Patrick Henry, they had worked valiantly in the cause of liberty.

Thomas Jefferson was tall and slender, with sandy hair, angular features and a ruddy complexion. His voice was calm and pleasant, his manner dignified.

"Major Clark, I am acquainted with your parents," Mr. Jefferson said.

George bowed. "Yes, sir. I have often heard my parents speak of you."

"If I am not mistaken, you were born in Albemarle County, not far from Shadwell, my own birthplace. But you are younger than I am, by nine or ten years. And your family moved from Albemarle to Caroline County when you were still a child."

"Your memory serves you well, sir," said George smiling. "It was just before my fifth birthday."

"Sit down, Major Clark," said Patrick Henry. "Now, sir, these gentlemen and I have pondered your proposal. A hard nut to crack, Major, an extremely hard nut! Healthy males of an age to bear arms are scarce in Virginia; we've packed them all off to General Washington. I do not know of any more who are available. And as for funds, we're scraping the bottom of the barrel, sir. But we realize that to expel the British from the western frontier would be a great triumph—one which might hasten the end of the war. So we are disposed to help you—to the extent that our circumstances permit."

"The legislature will appropriate six thousand dollars to finance your campaign," said Mr. Mason.

"You will be empowered to muster a company of three hundred and fifty men," said Mr. Wythe. "That is, if you can lay hands on them, Major."

"How many persons in Kentucky have been told of your plan?" Mr. Jefferson asked.

"Only five," George answered. "My two spies, and the three militia officers who will be my captains. They are Will Harrod, Leonard Helm and Joseph Bowman. I swore them all to secrecy."

"Yes, yes! Absolute secrecy must be the rule," said Governor Henry emphatically. "Let Hamilton at Detroit get wind of it, and from that instant the thing is doomed! Therefore, Major Clark, I shall issue two sets of orders to you. The first will be open to public inspection, a paper which authorizes you to take a body of troops to the defense of Kentucky. The second paper will be of a private nature, authorizing you to march on the British forts in Illinois. Keep both documents with you, but never show the second one except to your captains."

"Thank you, sir."

Governor Henry rose and gave George his hand. "By the way, I think that you had better command as *Colonel* Clark. I'll see that the legislature increases your military rank to that of a colonel."

"I am honored and most appreciative, sir," said George.

"Kaskaskia, Cahokia, Vincennes?" The Governor looked meditative. "Wilderness towns, Colonel Clark, with British flags flying above them. And you believe these flags can be lowered—and replaced by the Stars and Stripes?"

"I'm positive of it," George said, then repeated the word. *"Positive!"* . . .

But was he?

As he waited in Williamsburg for his orders and the new commission from the legislature, he had moments of doubt. He would be granted six thousand dollars with which to buy boats, weapons, ammunition, though he had estimated his expenses at three times that amount. He would be empowered to muster three hundred and fifty soldiers, and had been assured that perhaps not a single man was available.

80

It was a hazardous business—a hard nut to crack.

He wrote to Bowman, Will Harrod and Helm. They were to go to Redstone, a village on the Monongahela River. His army would gather there and in the spring embark for the West.

Having sent his letters, he felt more cheerful. In February he wrote again to Joseph Bowman.

"My hopes," he said, "are high."

Redstone was a popular embarkation point for travel on the western rivers. In the spring George went to Redstone and was greeted by Will Harrod.

"I've been here a week," Harrod said. "The early bird, eh? I've got some men with me. Not many, but some. Bowman and Helm are coming. Maybe they've had more luck with the recruiting; I hope so. And John Montgomery will join us with an outfit along the way."

George knew John Montgomery. "He can be my fourth captain. We'll go to Pittsburgh on flatboats, then down the Ohio to the falls, where we'll stop for a while."

Harrod said that there was a complication which perhaps he ought to mention. Fifty families of homesteaders had attached themselves to the expedition. The homesteaders had heard that George Rogers Clark was going to the defense of Kentucky, and since they had wanted to emigrate they thought this was their opportunity.

"Of course I couldn't tell them your real intentions," Harrod said.

"No, and it may be a good thing to have the homesteaders on our boats," George said. "If the Indians see the women and children, they may report to Detroit that we're just an ordinary emigrant party."

When Bowman and Helm appeared in May, George anxiously counted their straggling files.

"Well, we have a hundred and fifty men thus far," he said to Bowman.

"Montgomery will be at the falls," Bowman said. "He'll probably bring another fifty."

Two hundred recruits? . . . George looked them over. Lacking uniforms, they wore the usual frontier garb— fur caps, shirts and trousers of deer hide, moccasins or clumsy, homemade boots. Their weapons were those of the frontier, short-handled axes, tall rifles and long-bladed knives.

They were farmers, not soldiers. But all were young and alert.

"I'm satisfied with them, Bowman," George said. "Let's load the flatboats and pole out."

The weather was mild; the flotilla of boats slipped swiftly along the Monongahela, down the Ohio.

As he sighted the mouth of Limestone Creek, George thought of Joe Rogers. Standing on the boat deck with Captain Bowman, he talked about his cousin.

"I've grieved for Joe," he said. "I can't get him out of my thoughts. What could have happened to him? Was he tortured, scalped, killed?"

"Maybe not," Bowman said. "The Indians are sometimes very kind to their captives, and sometimes the captives become Indians. Yes, there have even been white men who became chiefs of tribes. Sometimes, too, a white captive is restored to his own people years later.

Don't despair of your cousin, Clark. You may see him again. Who knows?"

After two weeks on the Ohio, the boats were at the falls.

This stretch of water was really only a chain of rapids where the current narrowed to tumble and froth over a bed of rocks and boulders. Above the falls were several islands. At Corn Island the boats put into shore, the passengers alighted and began the construction of a camp.

Colonel Clark said that a blockhouse must be built. He had decided to leave the families of emigrants here, at least temporarily.

"These people have been our comrades," he said. "We can't abandon them without seeing that they have a place of refuge in the event of Indian raids."

While the building was in progress John Montgomery led twenty-five men to the falls.

"It's just half the number I figured on," Bowman observed to Clark. "But Montgomery's boys are all expert marksmen and full of spirit."

Clark nodded. Skill and spirit would be important factors in this venture.

As yet no announcement had been made of the little army's true destination. The recruits, as well as the emigrant families, believed that they were going to some section of Kentucky. Clark wondered what their feeling would be when he told them about the Illinois expedition. He would have to tell them soon.

I must make them understand how necessary it is to

83

seize the British forts, he thought. And I can't twiddle my thumbs much longer.

In June the blockhouse was roofed, the homesteaders were planting corn and a courier arrived on the island with news from Pittsburgh. Joyful news!—an alliance had been formed between France and the United States.

"If France is now on our side, it's time for plain speaking here, Captain," Clark said to Bowman. "Assemble the men. I'll speak my piece."

When the four companies with their captains were assembled, Colonel Clark "spoke his piece." He explained the purpose of his expedition. The first attack, he said, would be on Fort Gage in the town of Kaskaskia, which was on the Mississippi River. If successful there, he would then march on other enemy strongholds in the West. His soldiers would be fighting not merely to benefit and protect Kentucky, but also to help America win its war for independence.

"You're astonished, aren't you?" he said. "Yes, I can see that. But what I want to know is—are you going with me?"

The response was prompt, a roar of voices: "We're going with you, Colonel!"

On June 26 they started from Corn Island in the flatboats. The summer morning was warm, the sun glittered overhead. Before them were the seething rapids through which their awkward vessels must be maneuvered—or splintered on the rocks.

George was in the first boat to enter the rapids. He eyed the willow-fringed riverbanks. If Indians lurked among the trees, an alarm would be sounded—and his plan would have failed at the very outset.

He wished the sunlight were not so glaring. And suddenly it seemed to dim a little. He looked up. A black shadow was creeping across the sun, gradually obscuring it, turning day into dusk.

The men were bewildered. "The sun!" they cried. "It's fading! Something's wrong—"

"Pull your oars!" George shouted. "Pull! Shoot the falls!"

They bent to the oars; the boats jostled and twisted through the narrows, "shooting the falls." When the shadow lifted, the boats were well away from the boulders and into the river's broad current.

"But what was it?" the men asked.

"An eclipse of the sun," George said. "A total eclipse."

"An omen! A good omen, Colonel? Or bad?"

"Good, of course!" George smiled. *"To Kaskaskia! Forward, all!"*

## SURPRISE BY NIGHT

Where the Tennessee River flowed into the Ohio, Clark abruptly ordered the oarsmen to halt. He had glimpsed an empty skiff rocking in the shallows near the shore. Six men were seated on a sand bar beside the skiff.

"Bowman," he said, "do you see those people?"

"Yes. Who are they?" Bowman queried.

"I don't know, but I mean to find out. Stay here—and don't bring the boats in closer. I'll wade to the sand bar."

Clark slid into the water and waded. At his approach the six men got to their feet. He talked with them and then called to Bowman to have the skiff hitched to the rear of Harrod's boat. When this had been done, he waded back and hoisted himself into the lead boat again.

"Well," Bowman said, "what did they tell you, Colonel?"

"They say they're hunters—and good Americans. I have no reason to think otherwise, but I'm taking them with us, as a precaution. The fat, bald fellow is Duff. His story is that they've recently been deer-stalking around Kaskaskia. If so, they know the lay of the land there and might be useful to us. We'll drop downstream ten miles more to old Fort Massac and camp for the night. We can leave the boats at Massac and advance marching."

"I thought you said we'd go all the way to Kaskaskia by the rivers. Have you changed your mind?" Bowman asked.

"Yes, we're too exposed on the water. Suppose Duff and his friends were not hunters, but British agents. The jig would be up, wouldn't it? Massac is a hundred and twenty miles from Kaskaskia. We can make it in six days, and with no risk of being spied on."

Massac had once been a French post in the wilderness. Now it was the forlorn and ghostly shell of a fortress, its crumbling walls netted with vines. But Clark's men

87

were glad to land there and stretch their legs. Duff had game in his skiff. The meat was cooked and eaten.

"Stuff yourselves, boys," Clark advised, "and put the scraps in your pockets. It'll be slim pickings on the trail. We'll have no time or ammunition to squander in foraging."

Next day they marched through dense woods. The second day they were on swampy ground, where the woods thinned; the third morning they saw the prairie unfolding before them, a treeless, trackless region of grass as high as their heads.

Clark stopped. He did not know the prairie country; he had never traveled it. His captains were just as unacquainted with it. They stood and gazed at the sea of grass—grass billowing like waves in the slight breeze, billowing to the horizon.

Clark frowned. "We could soon lose all sense of direction here, Bowman. We need a guide. We should have brought a guide with us."

"What about Duff's party?" Bowman said. "Duff may have somebody. I'll ask him."

Bowman spoke to Duff and in a few moments a young man was saluting Clark.

"My name is Sanders, Colonel Clark. John Sanders."

"Are you a guide?"

"Well, sir, I've often been on the prairie," Sanders said. "I've guided Mr. Duff. I know where there's a path through the grass. I can show it to you."

"All right, show me," Clark said. "Go on, Sanders. We'll follow."

They followed for what seemed interminable miles.

Sanders stepped forward confidently—and then he faltered. Clark was quickly at his side.

"Where's your path, Sanders?"

"Well, sir, I don't see it. I'm a little—mixed up."

"Mixed up?" Clark's voice was stern. "Mixed up, eh?"

"Muddled, sir—"

"Muddled? Or pretending to be? Is this a ruse, Sanders? Have you tricked me? Was it your notion from the beginning that you'd get us into the grass and lose us? If it was, you'll pay for it with your life."

Sanders paled. "You—you'd kill me, sir?"

"How else are traitors to be dealt with? You told me that you would take us to a path. Go on, Sanders. Put us on the path."

Sweating and shivering, Sanders turned, plunged again into the swaying waves of high green grass. Clark gestured—and again the men followed.

After an hour of searching, Sanders cried: "I see it! The path!"

Yes, the path was visible now, like a trough between ocean breakers.

"So you're not a traitor, Sanders," Clark said. "You've proved your innocence. But mark this—and, men, all of you mark it! Our journey is no trivial thing. More is at stake than Sander's life, or mine or all our lives. I will tolerate neither deceit nor disobedience. Death is the penalty for both."

In the evening of July 4, they reached the steep bluffs of the Kaskaskia River. On the opposite bank the town, streets, houses and the spire of a church were clearly discernible.

A bell tolled for sunset.

"Kaskaskia is the biggest town in the West," Clark commented to Bowman. "The inhabitants are almost wholly French. That's Fort Gage, with the stockade around it. Philip de Rocheblave is in command. Rocheblave is a renegade Frenchman, a turncoat of the worst brand. Governor Henry described him to me as a tyrant; his own troops despise him. But Hamilton has promised that when England wins the war Rocheblave will be richly rewarded."

"England will never win the war," Bowman asserted.

Clark smiled. "No. Well, let's go down to the river. We've got to have rafts or barges, something to cross on. Tell the men to go quietly, no noise, and to lie in the underbrush until further orders. Oh, and one thing more, Bowman."

"Yes?"

"I'm not as heartless as I may seem at times. I hate bloodshed. I hate violence. I'll conduct this campaign as mercifully as I can."

"Yes," Bowman said. "I know."

They descended the bluff. Clark sent Ben Linn to scout for boats. Dusk fell; then it was night—and Linn returned to say that he had "borrowed" three dories and a cattle barge from a farmhouse near by:

"I peeked in the window at the farmer, sir. A funny little critter, ready for bed, in his nightgown. I didn't want to bother him, so I borrowed the boats. By crowding, we'll get the passel of us over in two trips, I figger."

"Thanks, Ben. Good work. Are you hungry?"

"Hungry? Am I?" Ben clutched his stomach. "Lawks!"

"We'll all have a big breakfast in Fort Gage," Clark said. "Right now I believe I'll chat with your farmer. I may learn something."

He went to the log house and knocked. The farmer opened the door, a candle in his hand.

"Who is it?" the farmer said. "Who—"

"A friend, sir. An American," Clark replied.

"American! *American!*" The farmer trembled; his knees quaked beneath his long nightgown; the candle shook and dripped tallow. "Ah, they've come! The Americans, the cutthroats, the demons! Oh, spare me, spare my poor wife, my children—"

"Hush!" Clark said. "You'll be spared. We're not demons. We've come to free you—"

But the farmer was slamming and bolting the door.

Clark shrugged. Evidently Rocheblave had been frightening the Kaskaskians, instilling into them a fear of all Americans and doing a thorough job of it—an impression which must be corrected. But at any rate, Clark thought, the townsfolk had not been forewarned; the American attack on Fort Gage would be a surprise, and thus according to plan.

The dories and cattle barge were rowed with muffled oars across the river. The men crawled out and up the sheer bluff. At the top Clark divided them into three groups. One group, led by Bowman, was to encircle the town. Helm and Montgomery with a detail of sixty would patrol the streets. Clark himself, with Will Harrod and twelve others, would invade the fort and demand Rocheblave's surrender.

"We must be fast, cautious and silent," Clark said.

"When I'm in control of the fort, Harrod will flash a torch on the stockade. As soon as you see the signal, fire your guns into the air and start yelling. Yell like demons. Tear through the streets, yelling. Make plenty of noise. Then meet me at the fort."

The three divisions dispersed. Clark, Harrod and their men crept toward the stockade. The gate was unlocked, creaking a little as they swung it. Somewhere a dog barked. Clark paused, listening, but the dog did not bark again; there was no other sound.

They slipped inside the gate and saw several low buildings, which were barracks and unlighted. Above them loomed the two-storied log fort, solid and dark except for the gleam of a lantern in one upper window.

As Clark's men crouched, rigid and listening intently, a sentry came into view, revealed by the shaft of lantern light, walking with slow, regular steps. Captain Harrod murmured; three men sprang and the sentry went down in a heap, stunned, his arms pinioned. From the fort a second sentry padded, hesitated then whispered: "Hi?" —but nothing more, for a gag was thrust into his mouth, his rifle was snatched and he was thrown headlong to the ground.

"Now," Clark said. "Now!"

They ran to the fort door; a dozen British troopers poured out and were overwhelmed, gagged and bound. Clark mounted a ladder stairway to the upper floor; his men swarmed at his heels. He seized the lantern, flung open a door.

Philip de Rocheblave was in bed, sleeping, snoring, his

92

wife beside him, his British uniform folded on the back of a chair, his wig on its stand on the table.

"Wake up! Wake up!"

Rocheblave sat up in bed, bewildered. "What? How dare you—who are you?" He shouted.

"I am George Rogers Clark, acting for Governor Patrick Henry, claiming this post for the United States of America. And you, sir, are my prisoner."

Rocheblave gasped and sputtered and reached for his wig, as if that might lend him dignity.

"Get up," Clark said, laughing. "Get into your britches. Your service here has ended. . . ."

Harrod set torches on the four corners of the square stockade. As the signals flared, a frenzy of yells, a volley of explosions, split the night stillness. At first it was only the Americans who caused such din and tumult; but soon the people of Kaskaskia were screaming and wailing, rushing from their homes into the streets, utterly terrified, milling about, shrieking questions in French: Were they all to be whipped, stabbed, maimed—murdered?

The questions went unanswered. These dreadful strangers, the soldiers dashing past, offered no explanation. The soldiers were hurrying in to the fort, where they continued to yell and fire their guns and wave lanterns from every window.

Toward morning the noise subsided. The Kaskaskians saw the British flag hauled down from Rocheblave's staff. They looked around and saw that nobody had been killed; there were no injured, no bloodstains anywhere, no houses destroyed, no property confiscated.

The Americans had come; they were in possession of

the town, the fort. That tall young man was their commander, the handsome one with the red hair. And what would he do here, that American Colonel Clark?

The Kaskaskians could not guess. They were puzzled.

# 11

# NEW FRIENDS -- AND DANGERS

At noon Clark sat at a table in the office which had been Rocheblave's. The day was sweltering hot. Clark had his shirt and boots off. He was unkempt, dirty, unshaven, his face streaked with soot. Since dawn he had been constantly busy. He had interviewed Helm and

Montgomery, telling them to keep the streets patrolled, but to forbid their guards to communicate with the excited householders. He had sent Bowman's company to Cahokia, a French and Indian trading post sixty miles north, with orders to occupy it. He had arranged for Rocheblave and the captured British garrison to be taken back to Virginia.

Now he was writing a report of last night's battle to dispatch to Governor Henry. . . . An odd battle, he reflected—and what a pity that all military engagements couldn't be of the same painless sort!

Captain Harrod entered the room.

"Visitors," Harrod said, saluting. "A delegation of citizens headed by Father Gibault. Want to see them?"

"Yes. Why not?"

Harrod grinned. "You look pretty fierce, half naked. You might scare them. They're plumb scared anyway, because they don't yet know what the shootin' was about."

"It won't hurt them to be a little scared," Clark said. "Do them good, in fact. Bring them in."

The Kaskaskians came in, five sober, elderly men and a Jesuit priest, Father Pierre Gibault. They stood uncertainly before Colonel Clark and he did not ask them to be seated. Father Gibault was the spokesman.

"We realize that our fate is in your hands," he said. "We think we may be exiled, or in some manner punished. We beg you to allow us to go to our church where we may pray and make our farewells."

Clark studied the priest's serious, saintly countenance; this was a man to be liked and trusted.

96

"You may pray in your church," Clark said. "I have no objections."

Father Gibault bowed; the five elderly citizens bowed and left the fort. Watching from the window, Clark saw them going into the church, followed by a throng of people.

Clark went to the bedroom in which Rocheblave had slept. He rummaged in the closet and found clean clothes, a tunic of soft yellow doeskin, a broad sash, a pair of loose white linen trousers. He bathed, shaved and dressed himself. As he was combing his hair, Harrod looked in.

"They're here again," said Harrod. "The delegation."

Father Gibault said that now they wished to beg for the greatest of favors. When they were sent into exile could it be done humanely, by families, husbands with their wives, children with their parents? And could they perhaps be permitted to carry with them some small bundles of personal belongings and mementos?

"We know there is war between England and America," the priest said. "But it has not touched us. We did not believe it ever would—and we have not considered the Americans as our enemies."

"You have considered us as demons, though—thieves, cutthroats, barbarians!" Clark exclaimed. "Why have you thought that? Why do you imagine that I might mistreat women and children, pull down churches? Oh, I know, sir. You were taught to think so; you had it drilled into you. The British told Rocheblave and Rocheblave told you. It is a lie, a conspiracy of lies, and you have been the victims! You are of French birth, are you not, sir?"

97

"I was born and educated in Canada, which was then a part of France," said Father Gibault.

"And your Kaskaskians are of French or Canadian ancestry? Well, do you know that France is now America's ally in the war with England?"

The priest had not known it. He stared; his companions stared.

"Oh, yes," Clark said. "That's a fact. You can believe it. France is contributing money, supplies and soldiers to the American Revolution. And believe this, too, sir: I will not interfere with the habits, customs or the religion of your people here. I regard myself not as their conqueror, but as their liberator. I shall also try to be their friend."

"Sir," said Father Gibault, "last night you surprised us greatly. Today you surprise us even more."

Clark had not misjudged the character of the priest or the townsfolk. When they heard that they were not prisoners, would not be mistreated or exiled, they were soothed. As their excitement waned they began to be respectful and courteous to the Americans, calling them the Big Knives and accepting them as their protectors.

Father Gibault frequently visited the fort and Clark always welcomed his visits.

"You have done so much for us," said the priest. "Can we do nothing for you, Colonel?"

"Yes," Clark said. "You can have the ladies of Kaskaskia make me a flag. The Stars and Stripes. I'll draw the pattern of it."

Father Gibault smiled gently. "The ladies are excellent seamstresses. You shall have twenty flags. But that is nothing! Perhaps later I may help you in some large measure. If so, command me."

Clark soon had word from Bowman. The captain had seized the villages of Prairie du Rocher and St. Phillipe. At Cahokia he had pacified the French residents and consulted with the chiefs of various Indian tribes.

These red men of the prairie had not been corrupted by the British, Bowman reported; they were willing to be on terms of truce with the Americans. But he had learned from them that Hamilton was sending guns and powder to the tribes on the Wabash.

"Vincennes is Hamilton's main stronghold in the West. He is scheming with the Indians in that area, encouraging them to pillage the white settlements. Look out for him!" warned Bowman, and added: "Though the garrison at Vincennes is quite small at present, it will be increased in the future."

Clark thought long about the information from Bowman. Some of it he repeated to Father Gibault, when the priest visited him again. He asked whether the Vincennes villagers were not all French, like the Kaskaskians.

"Oh, yes, and such good people," said Father Gibault. "I am their spiritual leader."

"Probably they have no understanding of the war."

"Probably not. No more than we had, before you came to enlighten us." Father Gibault seemed to meditate, then he said, "The garrison is small and weak at present? If you wish it, Colonel, I shall go to Vincennes and tell the people of the war and what has happened here."

"I do wish it," Clark said earnestly.

On July 14, with his five elderly companions, Father Gibault set out on horseback for Vincennes. On the first day of August he returned and hastened into Colonel Clark's office. He had ridden four hundred miles; his shabby black robe was dusty—but his fine eyes were shining.

Clark rose to shake hands with him. "Well, my friend?"

"You may indeed say 'Well!' " exclaimed the priest. "The American flag now flutters over Fort Sackville in Vincennes."

"What!" Clark was amazed.

"Yes, I had only to explain matters to my people on the Wabash. They are not stupid; they immediately saw that they must rid themselves of their odious oppressors. They went in a body to the fort and, as you had said, the British garrison was feeble. The citizens had brooms, rakes, scythes; they simply entered—and chased Hamilton's men out! I had with me a flag, the first of the new banners stitched by our Kaskaskia ladies. It was I who raised the Stars and Stripes to the top of the flagstaff!"

"My congratulations, sir," Clark said. "My warmest thanks."

Father Gibault beamed, and added: "Of course, I must see that an extra banner is made now. I guaranteed twenty—and twenty you shall have."

The Kaskaskians rejoiced with Colonel Clark at the news of their priest's valor at Vincennes. They had become entirely sympathetic with the rugged Americans who now controlled all the western outposts.

But Clark realized that this control was still a frail thing, that he still had much to do. He sent Captain Leonard Helm with twenty soldiers to hold the fort which the good citizens of Vincennes had so dramatically taken. He wrote to Governor Henry, asking whether Virginia could not furnish him some militiamen—even a few would be of the utmost assistance! He crossed the Mississippi River into Missouri, which was Spanish territory. At St. Louis, a fur-trading center, he talked with Fernando de Leyba, the Spanish governor, and with the wealthy merchant Francis Vigo.

De Leyba and Vigo were friendly to Clark.

"If you are set upon by Hamilton's Indians, we will aid you," said de Leyba.

"You think the raiders may be sent down from Detroit?" Vigo asked.

"I think so," Clark said. "There seems to be little danger from any other quarter."

"Ah, I am wary of them all—wherever they are."

"But the prairie tribes have vowed they will be at peace with us."

"They have vowed that?" De Leyba smiled ruefully. "Do not put your faith in it, Colonel. The savages make such vows only to renounce them. I suggest that you double your fists."

"Double my fists, sir?"

"Yes. Swagger, bluster, boast! Tell them that you have the power to shatter your enemies with one blow. You are more likely to attract them with a display of defiance than with softer methods."

101

Clark reflected upon De Leyba's suggestion. "Perhaps you are right," he said. "I'll ask Captain Bowman to call a council of the chiefs at Cahokia. And there I'll double my fists!"

# 12

## THE COUNCIL

The prairie tribes were curious about George Rogers Clark. There was not a western chief or brave who hadn't heard of him—this "Chief of the Big Knives" who now had called them to a council at Cahokia. Chippewa,

Kickapoo, Sauk, Fox, Ottawa, Potawatomi and Puan, painted and feathered, they flocked to the council.

Now they would see for themselves whether the tales of Clark's wisdom and fearlessness were true.

Bowman looked around their immense, sprawling encampment.

"A horde of savages," he said to Clark. "For each one of our men they have a hundred. In ten minutes they could wipe us off the face of the earth. We must never give them the opportunity, Colonel."

"Or the excuse," Clark said. "I'm thinking of how that can be managed."

The first day of the council the Indians paraded and feasted. The second day they danced and staged athletic contests between the tribes. Clark patiently watched the celebrations. He knew that the red men loved such ceremonies—and knew also that they were watchful and suspicious of him.

A French trader of Cahokia had invited Colonel Clark to use his cabin for the week. The cabin was at the edge of a shallow creek; on the other side of the creek the Puans had made their camp. The second night of the council, as Clark was resting on his bunk in the cabin, he heard the tread of his sentry along the creek bank— then cries and a great noise of scuffling and splashing.

He jumped up and shouted to the sentry: "Who's there?"

"The Puans, sir! They got past me. They were at the cabin door, meaning to kill you—"

Clark peered out. "I don't see them, sentry."

"They went back across the creek—"

"Well, after them! Put them in irons!"

The sentry whistled and a dozen guards came running. The guards waded the creek, ran into the Puan camp. The Puans were all lying on the ground, motionless under their blankets; they seemed to be asleep. The guards prodded and shook them. The Puans opened their eyes, yawned and said they had not stirred from their beds since early evening.

But a wet and muddy moccasin was protruding from beneath one blanket. The guards pulled at the blanket—and at several blankets, uncovering more wet moccasins. The wearers of the telltale moccasins were seized; iron fetters were clamped on their legs. With their chief they were taken to the village and into custody.

In the morning the chiefs of the other tribes apologized to Colonel Clark for the bad behavior of the Puans.

"We are blameless," these chiefs protested. "We would not break the truce. We hope that we shall not have to suffer the Big Knives' revenge."

Clark answered coolly: "It is of no consequence. I am a strong man. I do not care whether you are my friends or my foes. You have been celebrating here. Tonight I shall celebrate. Fiddlers will be fetched from Cahokia. My soldiers and the villagers will dance the night away!"

As the chiefs retired, they muttered among themselves: "He must indeed be strong—not bothering to number either friends or foes. And very bold—he must have a vast army, of which we see only the merest fraction. So when he speaks we will heed what he says."

That night the fiddle-strings squeaked, the villagers

105

and Clark's men danced gaily, with the colonel stepping the liveliest of them all.

> *"Green grow the rushes, O!*
> *Kiss her quick and let her go!*
> *But don't you muss her ruffles, O!"*

Clark hummed the tune, then said to Bowman: "It makes me think of my sister Ann—and home."

Next morning he summoned the tribes and stood before them, straight and tall. In one hand he held a belt of white beads, in the other hand a belt of blood-red beads. He ordered the guards to bring the fettered Puans to the meeting place.

"Take off their irons," he said.

When the irons were off he told the Puans that they must leave the council at once—but that they would not be pursued or attacked. Though they had sought to kill him, and thus had earned a sentence of death, he would not punish them. Americans, he said, were not cowards. Americans did not stoop to revenge.

Then he turned and said to all the tribes that he had not come to Cahokia to whine or to sue for peace with any nation. No, for he was a warrior. He did not ask the Indians to fight in his ranks—he did not need them, would not have them! This war was a white man's war, a war between the United States and England. The Indians must keep out of it, as noncombatants.

But if the prairie tribes had decided that they must oppose him—this was a different thing. If they were his enemies, he demanded that they fight him openly, as men of courage fight, not in darkness, not by tricks and treachery.

"And let us begin our fighting *now!*" he challenged.

He lifted the beaded belts so that all might see them.

"I have here two symbols. The white belt is peace, the red belt war. You must choose. Which do you choose?"

He tossed the belts on to the grass and folded his arms, waiting.

There was an interval of silence. Then in slow procession the chiefs shuffled forward and picked up the white belt of peace. The red one they trampled on disdainfully.

In October Clark went back to Kaskaskia.

"Have you a letter from Williamsburg for me?" he asked Captain Harrod.

"No, sir," Harrod said. "And nothing from Helm at Vincennes."

Clark was disappointed and vaguely anxious. Had Governor Henry forgotten him? And what was Captain Helm doing on the Wabash? By this time Hamilton must certainly have been told that the Americans were in Fort Sackville. Was Hamilton plotting mischief? If so, Helm's little band must soon be reinforced.

"And our men have never been paid for their soldiering, Harrod."

"Well, they're not beefing about it," Harrod said. "Not yet."

"They *will* be paid. I'll sign notes of credit on the state of Virginia; if the state doesn't honor the notes, I'll cash them."

107

"Do you have the money for that, Colonel?"

"No, but I can get it. I have a good deal of land—on the Ohio and in Kentucky. Fine, fertile tracts I claimed and cleared. I can mortgage my land for cash."

"And impoverish yourself? It doesn't seem fair," said Harrod.

"Yes, it is fair. Most of the men are married and have families. Their wives and children must be cared for. I'm not married. If I become poor as a church mouse, it will not matter."

The autumn season was warm, the weather beautiful, the western country serene.

Too serene! Clark thought moodily, and he wrote again to Patrick Henry and sent Ben Linn to Vincennes for news of Captain Helm.

As the autumn faded, winter winds ripped over the prairie, shriveling and rattling the bare boughs of trees, sweeping the people of Kaskaskia off the streets and into their snug dwellings. Every morning Clark went out to the stockade and scanned the horizon.

Where was Ben? What detained him?

Then snow fell and the town was snowbound. Occasionally Father Gibault plowed through the drifts to the fort for a chat with his friend Colonel Clark. Nobody else came.

But one day in December Captain Harrod said, chuckling, that there had been an arrival:

"You've been hankering for recruits, Colonel. I've got one for you. A young sprout from Virginia, from Caroline County. The wind blew him in."

"Caroline County! What's his name?"

Harrod's eyes twinkled. "Clark. Richard Clark. He brags that he's your brother—"

"He *is*! Where the deuce are you keeping him? Shoo him in!"

But the young sprout was already in, laughing and clasping the colonel's hand.

"Richard!"

"Hello, George." Richard was tall, dark haired and husky. "I enlisted as a militiaman in Williamsburg and came out here to join you."

"Why, Richard, you're—you're a man now!"

"I'm eighteen."

"Sit down. Talk to me."

They sat down together and talked. Richard had brought affectionate greetings from all the Clarks.

"You know, Richard," George said, "I've been homesick—terribly homesick, without realizing it."

"You look hale and hearty enough."

"Oh, my health is good. Nothing seems to affect it."

"And you've accomplished so much! That's what *you* must tell *me*."

Smiling, Colonel Clark told Richard about his expedition, the conquest of the Northwest, the taking of Kaskaskia—a victory achieved without the sacrifice of a single life, and about Bowman's good fortune in the scattered French villages, and the Indian council at Cahokia where the chief of the Big Knives had "doubled his fist."

"And here's something I haven't told anyone, Richard. Neither the men, nor my captains nor even Governor Henry—a part of my plan I've never disclosed. But I can tell you." He leaned toward his brother and spoke in a

109

low voice: "After I've reinforced Vincennes I'm going to Detroit to attack the British there, attack and lick them on their own stamping ground. As long as the British hold Detroit, our possession of these lesser forts is endangered. So I've got to have Detroit."

"How many Britishers are in Detroit?" Richard asked.

"A great many. But I've proved it isn't the size of an army that tips the scales; it's the mettle of the men. My men are the finest in the world—and they know the West as Britishers—foreigners—never could. I've sent my best scout, Ben Linn, to the Wabash, to reconnoiter and confer with Helm. When Linn returns with the report that all's well in Vincennes, I'll get squared away for the march on Detroit."

"It sounds splendid," Richard said. "When do you expect Linn?"

"Any day. Maybe today." Clark rose from his chair, went to the window and peered out. "Today may be the very day. . . ."

But Ben Linn did not return that day. The winter wore on and still there were no signs of that clever scout Ben Linn, no reports from Fort Sackville on the Wabash— until late in January, 1789.

Then Colonel George Rogers Clark heard that Linn was a prisoner in Vincennes, imprisoned with Captain Helm and the American garrison by Hamilton's men who had now regained the town and the fort.

110

# 13

## "ON TO VINCENNES!"

The St. Louis merchant Francis Vigo was the bearer of those doleful tidings.

In December Vigo had traveled along the Wabash. He was at Vincennes when Hamilton's army swooped down

111

from Detroit—two hundred redcoated British veterans and three hundred howling Indians, equipped with boats, cannon, unlimited amounts of small weapons and gunpowder.

Captain Leonard Helm, Ben Linn and the twenty Americans inside Fort Sackville knew nothing of the on-slaught until it confronted them. Captain Helm had scribbled a note to Colonel Clark. Ben Linn had crept out with the note and was intercepted and the note snatched from his grasp. Helm had looked right into the gaping mouths of the cannon, standing fast, refusing to surrender.

But all the circumstances were against Captain Helm. Redcoats and Indians had hurled themselves like an avalanche, and under its impact, the little party of defenders had fallen.

The British did not know what to make of Francis Vigo. Who was he? What was his errand in Vincennes? They had locked him up in the cellar of the fort. But later Hamilton had said that the merchant seemed to have no connection with the Americans. Hamilton had exacted a promise from Vigo to travel directly back to St. Louis and then released him.

This promise Vigo kept; he went from Vincennes to St. Louis—

"And now I've come to you, Colonel Clark, in Kaskaskia. I detest the British and owe them nothing in respect or allegiance. You I admire."

Clark summoned Bowman from Cahokia. In the small hours of the night they sat with Will Harrod and Montgomery in Clark's office, consulting.

Vincennes was two hundred miles away. The short route was overland, across low plains threaded by creeks and rivers which the winter weather had cloaked in ice and snow. The Drowned Lands, the region was called— and very aptly, too, for each spring when the ice and snow melted it was deeply flooded.

Vigo had said that Hamilton was remodeling Fort Sackville, digging trenches, building barriers around it, mounting his cannon in the blockhouses.

Could the Americans march to Vincennes now, in the most unpredictable season of the year, march through the Drowned Lands, which might be at their very worst? And suppose the Americans did complete the march, could they win a battle against Hamilton's superior force?

But Helm and his company were Hamilton's prisoners. They must be rescued.

"We'll go," Clark said. "What else can we do?"

The captains assented, "We'll have to go."

So they prepared.

Vigo was both wealthy and generous. He lent Clark the money with which to buy a flatboat, six cannon and a stock of supplies. The boat, christened the *Willing*, would carry the cannon and a crew of forty men down the Mississippi, up the Ohio, anchoring in the Wabash somewhere below Vincennes to await the overland marchers.

While carpenters worked on the boat, Clark called for volunteers—and wondered what the response would be.

The Kaskaskians were again in a turmoil—not frightened as they had been in the summer, but angry that Colonel Clark and his big gruff, gentle soldiers should be in such straits. The Kaskaskians had been liberated. They gloried in their liberty. Did they want that old Rocheblave or any tyrant like him plumped down into their midst again?

"No!" they declared emphatically, and went to the fort, a long line of them, to volunteer.

A lieutenant wrote their French names into the roster of the American regiment, as Clark looked on, touched at the sight. Only six months ago these people had been strangers to him. Now they would be his comrades-in-arms. He had carefully estimated his strength and how it must be distributed: forty men for the *Willing*, squads of guards left at Cahokia and Kaskaskia. With the French volunteers he would start for Vincennes in command of a hundred and twenty-seven troopers. . . .

Will Harrod came in, grinning.

"Sorry to disturb you, Colonel, but that boy is outside," Harrod said. "The one who was here yesterday, the little Frenchie who wants to go with us, as a drummer."

"A drummer? Well, drum music is inspiring. How old is the boy?"

"Just twelve. Seems to be a special chum of Sergeant DeWit's."

Clark thought about Sergeant Henry DeWit, the tallest of all the tall Americans, fantastically tall, towering above his mates.

"When I was twelve I felt that I could do anything," he said. "Anything! I guess this youngster has the same feeling. Let him sign up, Harrod, if his family doesn't forbid it. We could use a drummer. And tell DeWit to keep an eye on him. DeWit's a good chap, none better."

Clark got his pen and a sheet of paper. He must write to Governor Henry. How he wished that he might hear from the governor in this emergency! Recruits, funds, even a message of encouragement would mean so much.

I would bind myself to seven years of slavery in exchange for five hundred men, he thought.

But almost a year had elapsed and never an answer from Virginia.

Probably his other letters had never been received. He would not believe that Patrick Henry had ignored them.

So once more he wrote, making no requests now, expressing no hope that help would be given. Too late for requests and hoping! The letter, dated February 3, 1789, was merely an "intelligence," to acquaint Governor Henry with the endeavor—"on which," he wrote, "I am gambling my previous successes, the whole of my ambition. . . . I know the case is desperate, sir. But we must either quit the country or attack Hamilton, without loss of time."

On February 4 everybody in Kaskaskia went to see the launching of the *Willing*. Hats were waved, handkerchiefs fluttered. Soldiers and citizens shouted: *"Bon voyage, Willing! Good sailing! Au 'voir!"*

The day was fine. Clark gazed at the sun.

"Are you a sun worshiper, George?" Richard asked, jogging his brother's elbow.

"No, but I do dread rain," Clark said. "Rain could play hob with our march, Richard. Rain could be our ruination!"

The next day was cloudy, February 5, the day of departure.

115

"Don't fret about the clouds, George," Richard said. "One gust of wind could snap them away."

The ladies of Kaskaskia presented Colonel Clark with the flags they had made for him, the twenty flags of red, white and blue, the Stars and Stripes. And the ladies had cooked a dinner for the regiment. They spread the feast on trestle tables in the schoolhouse: platters of fried fish and pork, bowls of cabbage and baked beans, apple sauce and Indian pudding.

The soldiers ate and laughed, joked and drank toasts in mugs of cider—toasts to the colonel and the captains. Then Father Gibault got up to bestow a blessing, while all heads were bowed. The priest's thin, sensitive face was suffused with emotion as he prayed a lengthy prayer, invoking God's loving kindness for these men who would fight for the freedom of human beings everywhere.

At three o'clock in the afternoon Colonel Clark, the captains and the men went out into the street. The flags were unfurled. The drummer brought his sticks down with a preliminary flourish: *Rat-tat-tat!*

"Forward march!" Clark's voice rang loud and firm. "To Vincennes!"

Briskly they marched, and the Kaskaskians wept to see them go:

*"Vive, Colonel Clark! Long live the regiment!"*

One mile above the town Clark's men ferried the Kaskaskia River and soon were on the St. Louis Trace, an old road winding like a frayed ribbon toward the Wabash. Five miles more, then it was dusk, rain was drizzling. The men ate a cold supper and slept on the dank brown grass. During the night the rain stopped, but the morning was gray and ominous.

The second day's march was longer; the third day the marchers put thirty-five miles behind them, doing as well the fourth day. The clouds hung heavily, showers spattered intermittently; creeks were swollen to twice a normal size and pools of water spotted the level prairie.

The men said they reckoned it'd been pouring somewhere close by: "Reckon we're in for a good wetting."

But they said it cheerfully. Even when the pools encroached upon the road, glazing the surface with black mud, weighting their boots with mud, they did not grumble. They had ample food; their rifles crackled, bringing down squirrels, pigeons, wild turkeys. Each night they gathered at the campfires, drinking hot, sweet coffee, spinning yarns. Afterward, rolled in their damp blankets, they slept soundly on the sodden ground.

They came to the halfway point of their march. Then the showers were more frequent, the pools wider and deeper. The prairie resembled a pond spaced with small islands of hummock. The road was submerged, marked only by the Indian signs blazed on the trunks of trees a century ago. There was no game to bag here, for the flood had driven out birds and animals. The men sloshed forward, soaked to the skin, some of them sneezing and coughing. At night they ate hardtack. The campfires sputtered and gave off little heat or light.

At the Petit River Clark halted.

The Petit, usually a placid stream, had burst its banks.

"We'll have to cross on rafts," Clark said.

In torrents of rain, trees were cut down, the logs hewed

117

and rafts constructed. More rafts were built at the Saline River. The crossings were made against a lashing wind and through water which boiled and whirled—but made without accident.

Beyond the Saline, at Cat Plain, Clark halted again. Cat Plain was a lofty, narrow plateau, fifteen miles in length, five miles wide. A relic of the age of glaciers, it lay like a gnarled finger above the prairie.

"Buffalo are often to be found on the plain," Clark said. "We may find some there now, refugees from the flood."

The men were pleased, for their stomachs growled from hunger. They climbed the walls of the plateau and flushed a herd of buffalo on the heights. They shot two of the great lumbering beasts and that night had a huge and savory meal.

But now they faced the Drowned Lands, by far the most difficult stretch of all.

"Sixty-three miles," Clark said to Bowman. "If the rain would just hold off—"

Bowman shook his head. "I've never known *wetter* rain."

"No." Clark smiled grimly. "Well, what can't be cured must be endured, Captain. We'll take the Drowned Lands by stages—the Little Wabash River, the Embarrass, then on to Mammelle Hill. There's a sugar camp beyond Mammelle Hill and we can rest in the maple grove, it's high and should be comparatively dry. We'll need to rest, for then we'll have the bottom lands of the Big Wabash in front of us."

"And the worst of the flood," Bowman said. "We're a week out from Kaskaskia."

Richard was standing with his brother and Bowman.

"A week? Seven days!" Richard exclaimed. "It seems longer."

"Are you sorry you came, Richard?" Clark asked.

"No," Richard said. "No, and I somehow think you'll pull us through."

On February 13 they reached the Little Wabash. On February 17 they marched to the juncture of the Embarrass River and the Big Wabash. Each day had been like the one before: tedious hours of floundering and splashing in gray water under a gray sky—rain, mud, the wind blowing a gale, the temperature dropping.

The men were cold, weary—and on scant rations, too; that meal of buffalo meat at Cat Plain was only a tantalizing memory. Hardtack, a lump of brown sugar, a handful of parched corn was the daily fare, a starvation diet. And no shelter at night, no shelter at any time.

Yet they continued to advance doggedly, though the water lapped at their knees, their waists, their armpits. Where the flood was deepest, they carried their guns above their heads. The weapons must not be damaged!

The men toiled up Mammelle Hill and the rain slacked. The day was freezing cold, ice forming like a film of glass on the country below. A fire was made and the men tried to dry themselves, their blankets and the twenty beautiful banners brought from Kaskaskia.

Clark looked for the *Willing*.

"It should be somewhere around here," he said. "I don't see it. Perhaps it's stranded downstream."

He had two of the men make a pirogue, a rude sort of canoe which was nothing more than a log with the center pulp scooped out and the ends sharpened. He sent the men down the Wabash in the pirogue to search for the *Willing,* but it was nowhere in sight.

The marchers spent the night on Mammelle Hill. They had no supper, slept because they were exhausted and at daybreak were roused by the faint echoes of a booming cannon.

"The morning gun at Fort Sackville," Clark said, and he sent out the pirogue again. If the *Willing* was stranded, surely some of its crew and cargo might be salvaged.

The searchers returned at noon—without any salvage from the *Willing,* or word of its mysterious fate. Had it been swamped, captured, sunk? Would anyone ever know? But the men in the pirogue had a party of five hunters in tow. The hunters were Frenchmen, residents of Vincennes. They had a freshly killed deer in their rowboat—and they were utterly astounded at the sudden appearance of this small bedraggled army on Mammelle Hill.

Clark talked with them, asking questions which they answered reluctantly at first, then with a growing eagerness.

The hunters said that the British in Vincennes had not the slightest knowledge of the Americans' approach—they did not dream of it! The villagers, they said, disliked Hamilton and his insolent redcoats. One and all, they would assist Colonel Clark in his attack. And there were Indians on the Wabash who would fight against Hamilton.

"The Piankashaws, sir," they told him. "Their chief is

The Tobacco's Son. A good Indian, a great chief. The Tobacco's Son has said that the Americans are his friends. He will join your army."

"No," Clark said. "I don't have Indians in my army."

The hunters were still more astounded. "Perhaps The Tobacco's Son may render you some other service."

"How far are we from the sugar camp, gentlemen?" Clark asked.

"Four miles, sir."

"Then we can get there by dusk. Early tomorrow we march on Fort Sackville."

"March?" The hunters gasped. "It cannot be done! Why, sir, you would have to cross Horseshoe Plain! Nine miles of water! A bog, a morass, and the ice an inch thick on it! No, no, you can never cross Horseshoe Plain tomorrow. You can never cross it at all on foot!"

Clark looked keenly at his gaunt, hollow-eyed men.

"I think we can," he said. "And now, gentlemen, we'll relieve you of the deer in your rowboat. One deer is not enough for so many of us, but it may appease the gnawing pain under our belts. You can accompany us to the sugar camp or remain here, as you wish."

The next day was cold but bright: no rain, no clouds— for a wonder the sun shone! The sugar camp was on an elevation at the edge of Horseshoe Plain. Early in the morning Clark and Bowman stood on the elevation's east slope and gazed down at the plain.

"Four miles out from this place is a wooded ridge," Clark said. "Three miles beyond the ridge is a small hill which the Indians call Warrior's Island. Two miles beyond Warrior's Island is Vincennes."

Bowman nodded. "Nine miles in all."

"Yes. When we get to Warrior's Island we'll be safely out of the flooded area. We'll be able to see the roofs of the town and can definitely plan our attack on Hamilton."

"Will we take the nine miles by stages, Colonel?"

"Yes, and the first stage is from the sugar camp to the ridge. The men are tired; some are too weak to walk; some are actually sick with chills and fever. We'll put the sick men into the pirogue and the hunters' boat. The others will march. How's our young drummer?"

"The little Frenchie? He's in good shape. A stout lad," Bowman said. "He has stuck to the grind and never a whimper out of him."

"Tell him to be watching me—that's a special order. If I signal, he's to beat his drum—fast and loud. And, Bowman, I want you to march in the rear, at the tail end of the line. Have your gun primed. If any man turns back, shoot him."

Bowman recoiled, protesting. "Shoot? No, Colonel—"

"Yes, Captain," Clark said. "I give the command for the sake of the men themselves. We're in enemy territory now. We can't retreat, we can't stay on this exposed elevation. We must go forward, all of us. There is no alternative."

"But, Colonel, not a man in the regiment *would* turn back—unless he was ill, crazed by the lack of food and the bitter weather, temporarily out of his mind—"

"I know that," Clark said. "And in that case, it would

122

be more humane to take his life than to leave him here to die wretchedly and alone, or to be scalped and killed by the Hair Buyer's Indians. I have given the command, Captain. You will comply with it."

"Very well, sir," said Bowman.

Clark then spoke to the men. He told them to brace for this final effort of their long and grueling journey. The sick, he said, would have passage; those who might fall during the crossing would be picked up by the pirogue and the rowboat.

The men listened in silence. They seemed resolute.

Clark descended the slope to the plain. The men followed, their boots splintering the water's icy coating. Only a few of them boarded the pirogue and the boat. Captain Bowman assumed his position at the rear of the procession.

Clark ordered two men to step into the lead and make soundings of the flood's depth. These two had poles with which they poked and probed the water, shouting, "Ho, firm base, advance!"—and sometimes, "Ho, sinkhole, beware!"

The marchers plodded valiantly toward the wooded ridge, four slow, terrible miles. When at length they were there, many had not the strength for clambering up the scrubby bank, but staggered and sprawled and were dragged up by their stronger comrades.

"Rest," Clark told them. "Lie down. Relax a bit. We're only three miles from Warrior's Island. And what's that to us, eh? Three miles? Nothing!"

They rested briefly, then plunged again into the icy torture. Now the flood washed around them, colder than ever, numbing their feet and legs. Clark saw that many were lurching, falling. The pirogue and rowboat were full; men were clutching at the oars, hanging to the sides.

Abruptly Clark stooped, smeared his face with water. He spilled a pinch of gunpowder from his pouch into the palm of his hand and smeared the black powder over his face from brow to chin.

"Whoo-oo-oop!" he yelled. *"Whoo-ee!"*

He signaled to the drummer boy. Instantly the drum was beaten—loud and fast: *Rat-tat-tat!*

"Whoo-oop! *Whoo-ee!"*

The soldiers stared. Their colonel, it seemed, had gone mad! Look at him, doffing his cocked hat, waving the hat, tossing it in the air, prancing, strutting, in grotesque imitation of an Indian war dancer—his face blackened like an Indian's, and that wild, savage cry: *"Whoo-oop-ee!"*

And tall Sergeant DeWit—what was *he* doing? Why, DeWit had grabbed the drummer boy, the little Frenchie, and whisked him up astride his shoulders! And there he sat, the drummer boy, pounding out a steady, rhythmic *Rat-tat-tat*—and singing, yes, singing in a clear, young voice:

> *"Yankee Doodle came to town,*
> *Riding on a pony—"*

Yankee Doodle, eh? . . . The men stared, then they chuckled. It was comical, like a show you might see in a theater, like a circus with clowns and jesters. Some of the men began to sing with the drummer; some whooped with the prancing colonel.

So, forgetful of cold and danger, they marched with renewed hope and energy across those last three miles of Horseshoe Plain to the haven of Warrior's Island.

# THE BATTLE

It was February 23, midafternoon.

From Warrior's Island Clark peered at the clustered roofs of Vincennes and thought of the French villagers. They're not fond of the British, he thought. They may

126

assist us. At any rate they must be warned of our coming.

The note which he wrote to them was friendly in tone: Those inhabitants of the town who loved liberty were to shut themselves into their homes, where they would not be disturbed. Those who loved the English king could repair to Fort Sackville, unite with Hamilton and prepare for battle.

Having dispatched a messenger with the note, he ordered that twenty slender maple saplings be cut and trimmed.

"We have three more hours of daylight and might as well go on," he said to his captains. "But we may be seen now, so we must be seen to advantage. Get our twenty banners tacked to the saplings. Spread out the line and space the banners along it. I want the flag-bearers to raise the colors high and flourish them. By marching and countermarching, we'll have the appearance of a mass of troops, twenty companies—each with its flag."

Marching and countermarching, single file, the men jogged obliquely forward, the sunshine slanting on their flourished banners, and halted at dusk, for the messenger was back with his report.

The people of Vincennes were all in their homes—not one had gone to the fort, the messenger told Colonel Clark.

"And they have presents for you, sir," he added. "Some time ago Hamilton ordered them to bring him any powder and ball they possessed. They did not obey the order. Instead they buried the stuff in their yards and cellars. Now they're digging it up and will give it to you."

"Good!" Clark said. "We need ammunition almost more than food."

"Oh, as to that, sir, we'll have food, too. The village women are cooking soup, the baker is baking bread for us."

The messenger described Fort Sackville. It was on the river, he said, and very like the Kaskaskia fort in structure—a large blockhouse at the center of a parade ground, enclosed by a stockade which had smaller blockhouses at the four corners. The British garrison was quartered in the large blockhouse.

"And that's probably where Helm and Linn and our other Americans are imprisoned," Clark said. "I'll send a squad to fire on the stockade's west wall. The main part of my force I'll swing to the gate side and attack there."

Soon fourteen men started off through the darkness toward the stockade. A few minutes more and a round of shots sounded, sudden and fierce. Clark led his troops into a marshy pasture near the gate—and heard someone in the shadows speak his name: "Colonel Clark?"

It was The Tobacco's Son, chief of the Piankashaws. He stepped out, big and blanketed. He carried a cloth bag which seemed to be heavy.

"Sir," said The Tobacco's Son, "I have one hundred warriors ready to fight with you against the hated British."

Clark replied very courteously: "I wish I could accept them, sir. But we are the Big Knives; we fight our own battles. And this is not the red man's war."

"You think not? Hamilton has many more Indians than

whites. Yes, even now Lamothe is out seeking Indians for Hamilton."

"Lamothe? Who is he?"

"A British captain," said The Tobacco's Son. "It is expected that Lamothe will return to the fort tonight. He will come from the hills and he may be bringing in a hundred recruits. Have a care that Lamothe does not hem you in between Hamilton's cannon on the one hand and these recruits on the other."

"We'd then be in something of a jam, eh?" Clark nodded. "Excellent advice, sir. I'll remember it."

"This bag contains gunpowder, a token from the people of Vincennes—I was asked to fetch it to you." The Tobacco's Son deposited the bag at Clark's feet. "Perhaps I can get more powder for you. I shall try."

As Clark thanked The Tobacco's Son and saw him step again into the shadows, a roar of cannon fire burst from the four blockhouses at the corners of the stockade.

"Well, the battle is on!" Clark told his captains. "Let the Hair Buyer's cannon bark. His redcoats are poor marksmen. Where they blast, we'll snipe. Tell our boys to go into action. Tell them to watch the blockhouse windows—whenever a window is pushed ajar for the snout of a cannon, pour in a hail of bullets!"

The Americans trotted toward the stockade and encircled it, their rifles flashing. As they ran, they yelled and howled with all the breath in their lungs. They watched the blockhouses and when the British cannon boomed, they ducked behind trees and fences, out of range. Then, with amazing accuracy, they sent a volley of lead through the open windows. Knowing that they had not much ammunition, certainly none to waste, they made each shot count. The frantic din of their shots and shouting continued—until Clark silenced it with a command.

Lamothe was coming.

"Quiet! Keep down! Let Lamothe pass unchallenged!"

Lamothe had thirty-five Indians following him. On moccasined feet they crept through the hushed streets, unaware of the Americans hiding so near them. They crept to the stockade. A lantern flared above them, revealing the British captain's uniform, the war paint and feathered bonnets of his savage allies. Ladders were lowered from the blockhouses. Lamothe and his recruits began to climb the ladders.

Someone among Clark's men laughed loudly. Someone else hooted scornfully. A chorus of laughter and catcalls rose from the American lines:

"*Whoo-oop! Whoo—ee!*"

Lamothe and his Indians were dumbfounded. Their ladders swayed and teetered. In great confusion they climbed hurriedly, jumping and falling in their rush to get over the stockade and into the fort.

"Don't shoot, boys!" Clark shouted. "Hold it! We'll take 'em, the whole shebang—and the Hair Buyer, too! We've got lots of time!"

By midnight the American army had been strengthened. The citizens of Vincennes were venturing into the streets, bringing more parcels of powder, bringing food. Some were volunteering to fight in the American ranks. At dawn Clark sent a messenger to the stockade gate with a white flag and a letter for Colonel Hamilton.

The letter demanded Hamilton's instant surrender.

If I am obliged to storm, you may depend upon the treatment due to a murderer. If you destroy stores of any kind, or any papers, or hurt one house in the town—by heaven, there shall be no mercy shown you.

At ten o'clock the messenger returned with Hamilton's answer. It was curt and uncompromising. He would not surrender. "I am not disposed to be awed into any decision unworthy of a British subject."

Clark read the few words and gestured to his captains. "All right. Resume the bombardment."

The American rifles were trained again on the fort. For an hour they flashed, volley after volley, with deadly aim. Then a British soldier with a white flag was seen edging through the gate.

Bowman intercepted the British soldier as he picked his way toward Clark.

"Here's a second note from Hamilton, Colonel," Bowman said. "Maybe the Hair Buyer *is* a little awed. We've made him believe we're not to be trifled with."

Clark read the second note. "Hamilton wants me to confer with him just outside the gate."

"Don't do it! Don't go. It could be a plot to grab you as a hostage."

"Oh, I don't think so," Clark said. "I'll confer with him —but in front of the village church, in full sight of our men. Tell the messenger I'll meet Hamilton there. And you come with me, Bowman."

Several minutes later, in full sight of the men, Clark and Bowman walked to the church. Soon Hamilton and his aide Major Hay emerged from the stockade. The scarlet jackets and trousers of the British officers, their white waistcoats and burnished boots, were in sharp contrast with the soiled and shabby attire of the two Americans— a contrast which Clark's troopers were quick to observe and ridicule.

"Dressy feller, that Hair Buyer!" they scoffed. "Ain't he purty, though? Ain't he *clean*? Ain't they both jist *lovely*?"

Hamilton disregarded the scoffing. He handed Clark a sheet of paper.

"My terms, sir," he said. "I will release Captain Helm, Ben Linn and the other rebel prisoners. I will evacuate Fort Sackville. You must then permit me to move my army, all of it, to Florida, where we have friends. The terms are fair. You will, of course, agree to them."

Clark shook his head. "I will not agree, sir."

Hamilton flushed angrily. "What more do you ask?"

"I have told you," Clark said. "Immediate and unconditional surrender. It is a demand, not a request. My men, sir, are at such a pitch of fury that they would like to tear down the stockade and fort and wipe out your garrison. I have no idea how long I can restrain them."

Hamilton looked at the American line. He frowned— and Major Hay was trembling.

"In my opinion," Clark said, "the spilling of any more blood on this ground would be murder. Others have been guilty of murder. I have no wish to be."

Hamilton looked at the paper which Clark had re-

132

jected. "Very well," he said, "we will fight it out to the last."

Clark bowed. "That is for you to decide, sir. I shall order my drummer to beat the alarm. When five minutes have elapsed, we will storm you."

The British officers unlatched the gate and Hamilton paused.

"Colonel Clark, I insist upon knowing why you are so harsh!"

"Harsh, sir? If I seem harsh, it is because you have loosed the red barbarians on the people of the Northwest, bribed them to massacre innocent homemakers and their women and children. When I consider the cruelty of your Indian hirelings I can perfectly understand the vengeful feelings of my soldiers."

"That is not true!" Hamilton exclaimed.

"It is quite true, sir."

"I have done nothing but what my superiors counseled."

Clark shrugged. "I have no information about the counsel of your superiors. *My* counsel is that you retire into the fort and listen for our drumbeat."

As Hamilton hesitated at the gate, rifles blazed from the crest of a hill behind the American line. Down the hill, straight into the midst of the Americans raced eight Indians, shrieking like a pack of wolves.

What was it?

"A trap!" Bowman cried. "We're betrayed!"

"No!" Hamilton protested. "No! The Indians are my raiders, sent a week ago to the Ohio country. Don't fire on them! They know nothing of our battle, our truce. Don't let your men fire—"

"Run back, Bowman!" Clark shouted. "Tell the men to hold fire!"

Bowman ran. But Clark's men had leveled their guns, whipped out their big knives. They charged at the raiders, killed them and tossed the limp bodies into the muddy floodwater of the Wabash.

Hamilton shuddered and leaned upon the shrinking, pallid Major Hay.

"Colonel Clark," he muttered. "I will surrender on your terms."

"I didn't want it to end like that," Clark said later to Bowman. "The killing of those Indians was violence of a sort I have condemned in the British and never practiced myself."

"But can you blame our men? No, sir" Bowman argued. "They heard the whistle of bullets, the hideous shrieking. They saw bloody scalp locks dangling from the raiders' belts. What were they to think except that it was a counter-attack, more of Lamothe's rascals arriving? And their violence hastened Hamilton's surrender. It may have forestalled a long and costly siege here, the loss of many more than eight lives."

"But still I am sorry for it," Clark said.

# 15

## A GLORIOUS DAY,
## AND AFTERWARD

February 25, 1779, was sunny and breezy, a day like
spring. By ten o'clock in the morning all the people of
Vincennes were up and out to see the solemn ceremony

of Colonel Hamilton's surrender to Colonel Clark. Two by two, Clark's men marched toward the old fort on the bank of the Wabash.

*"Vive les Americains!"* cheered the watching throng. *"Vive, Colonel Clark! Bravo!"*

At the stockade the marchers stopped and stood at attention. The gate opened. Hamilton, his officers and garrison filed stiffly through and passed between the two American columns. When the last redcoated soldier was in the street, Clark with half his regiment marched into the fort's empty enclosure, leaving Captain Bowman and the other half outside.

Then Hamilton, looking very unhappy, walked back to the gate and shut it. In this way the British commander acknowledged his defeat. Fort Sackville had become the property and responsibility of Hamilton's conqueror.

The British colors had been removed from the staff on the parade ground. Now the biggest of Clark's banners was affixed to the cords and pulled to the top of the flagstaff. The breeze lifted and flaunted the folds of the Stars and Stripes. The cannon in the blockhouses thundered thirteen deep-throated salutes, one detonation for each of the states.

As the noise of the cannon subsided, Clark spoke:

"Men, the victory is your achievement, not mine," he said. "I thank you in the name of the Continental Congress and of the Commonwealth of Virginia, which you have so loyally served and honored. Your deeds here will be remembered." He paused, then added: "This post has been Fort Sackville. Henceforth it will be Fort Patrick

Henry. And may peace and freedom prevail within its walls forever!"

There was a silence, then tremendous rejoicing:

*"Fort Patrick Henry! Hurrah for the Continental Congress and George Rogers Clark!"*

All day and all the next week Vincennes was in gala mood. Hamilton's prisoners, including Captain Helm and Ben Linn, were enthusiastically welcomed back into the regiment. And one afternoon a flatboat nosed ashore— the *Willing!*—neither captured nor sunk, but only delayed by the flood, and landing now with crew, guns and ammunition stock in good condition.

The men on the *Willing* were sorry that they had missed the battle. They told how their boat had been tossed about, battered by wind and rain, narrowly escaping ruin. Somewhere along the way they had picked up a lone, lost traveler, a messenger from Governor Henry in Williamsburg with a letter for Colonel Clark.

"The governor thinks you're still in Kaskaskia, sir," the messenger said to Clark. "I was trying to deliver the letter to you there when the floods came up. A lucky thing your boat crew rescued me. Lucky for me—and maybe for you, also."

Governor Henry wrote that he had just learned of Colonel Clark's gallantry at Kaskaskia; he expressed his gratitude and that of the Virginia legislature. In the spring he would send five hundred men to Colonel Clark, so that the conquest of the Northwest might be continued. Captain Bowman's ability had been recognized by the legislature, too: "Joseph Bowman," the governor wrote, "is promoted to the rank of major."

As he studied the letter, Clark thought of the campaign he wished to make against Detroit. Indeed, he was always thinking of it now. He had discussed it with his captains and he had their approval.

"Five hundred Virginians," he commented to Major Bowman. "And Montgomery says three hundred more may be raised in Kentucky. Eight hundred men? A nice, sizable lot of troops. But ought the move on Detroit be postponed until spring? I feel in my bones that we should go at once."

Bowman smiled. "You feel it in your bones, eh? Well, can't we?"

"No, that's the devil of it," Clark sighed. "The best we can do is to get the Virginians and Montgomery's Kentuckians to meet here on the Wabash as early as possible. Let's say in June. I'll set the date. Then in the summer we can start north."

Meanwhile he had various affairs to see to.

In March he sent Colonel Hamilton and his humbled officers to Williamsburg, where they would be jailed by the military authorities for the duration of the war. Hamilton had drawn many of the French residents around Detroit into his army: these men Clark released, requiring only that they swear never to fight for England again. He gave them guns, food and canoes and told them to go home.

"Go home and consider the reasons for the Revolution," he said. "I believe that when you have considered well, you'll be converted to the American cause."

The defeat of Hamilton was having its effect upon the Wabash tribes. Shocked at first, they soon were anxious to make friends with the Big Knives occupying

Fort Patrick Henry. The chiefs of the Ouiatenons, Miamis and Potawatomis came to smoke the peace pipe with this tall Colonel Clark, who seemed to dare everything and fear nothing.

"Take us under the cover of your wings," they begged.

Clark did not turn the Indians away, but he would not rely on them. He knew that the promises they offered so easily might as easily be forgotten.

He was more concerned with wondering how he could obtain money with which to pay his men for their services as soldiers.

"The state of Virginia has never yet paid them," he said to his brother Richard.

"Or you, either," said Richard.

"Oh, I have no pressing need for money. The men have. Last year I mortgaged some of my land for cash and distributed it among them. It was so little though, compared with what's owed to them."

"Will the state of Virginia reimburse you, George?"

"I've registered a claim for reimbursement; perhaps I'll get it. But that will take time. The question in my mind is whether, without pay, the men will be in favor of the Detroit expedition."

"So you're really going to Detroit?" Richard asked.

"I hope to go," Clark said. "More than anything in the world I want to attack and seize Detroit."

Another question to which he devoted much thought was the future of the Illinois country. Now that the British had been driven out, the people had no government. He wrote to Governor Henry: "Illinois should be a county of Virginia, as Kentucky is, with laws and courts, judges and an organized militia." Governor Henry agreed, and replied that the matter would be submitted to a vote of the House of Burgesses.

But this, Clark knew, would also take time. He recalled the tedious months he himself had spent long ago, pacing the Williamsburg cobblestones, waiting for the members of the House of Burgesses to vote a government for Kentucky. They were as slow as snails!

One morning he talked with Major Bowman and Captain Leonard Helm.

"Our French comrades-in-arms are pining to return to Kaskaskia," he said. "I'll send them on the *Willing*—and since I have no urgent tasks at present, I'll sail with them. I'm stationing a small permanent garrison in Fort Patrick Henry. You will command it, Major Bowman, in my absence. Captain Helm, you will guard the town."

In bright, mild weather the *Willing* sailed. The floods had receded, the voyage was pleasant; and at Kaskaskia Clark and his soldiers were received with wild applause, tears, music, feasting and dancing. From Cahokia and neighboring villages the inhabitants flocked to join in the celebrations.

"We're heroes, George," Richard said, laughing and delighted with the merrymaking. "And you are the very idol of Kaskaskia."

"Am I?" He had no desire to be a hero, an idol. He was restless, thinking of Detroit.

On May 12 a communication from Williamsburg reached him. The House of Burgesses had acted with unusual speed. Illinois was now a county of Virginia and would shortly be able to form its government and elect its officials.

This was important news! Standing on the steps of

Father Gibault's church, Clark read it aloud to the Kaskaskians.

That evening he said to Father Gibault: "In a few days I'm going back to Vincennes. Our people here will be safe in your keeping."

"Ah? You have work to do in Vincennes?" the priest queried.

"A work of planning. I shall gather up the remnants of my old army and await some new recruits."

"And then—more triumphs for history to record, Colonel?"

He smiled and said fervently: "I hope so, sir."

In Fort Patrick Henry he sat waiting, waiting for those new recruits. Although Montgomery had assured him of three hundred, only thirty reported. Five hundred were to have come from Virginia; only one hundred and fifty ever arrived.

He was sorely disappointed. What must he do now? And as he brooded and tried to readjust his plans, an accident occurred at Fort Patrick Henry.

In the cellar of the fort a powder magazine exploded. Major Bowman was fatally hurt, and died of his injuries within a few days.

Clark was stunned by Bowman's death. Big stalwart Bowman, the most loved and faithful of his friends!

"How can I go on?" he asked himself. "How march against Detroit—without Joseph Bowman?"

The fact was that he could not march against Detroit in this summer of 1779 and he admitted it grudgingly. He did not have enough men; he did not know where

141

more were to be found. In July and August, and then in the months of autumn, he made a thorough canvass of the Illinois and the Kentucky country, but failed to rally enthusiasm for his new campaign.

Somehow the people seemed to have lost interest in the American Revolution. They seemed to believe that with the victory at Vincennes the war was over—yes, and won, too!

Even some of Clark's veterans who had followed him for years were dropping away, going back to their farms and families. In time of stress they had fought like lions; if threatened, they might fight as bravely again. But the West was quiet now.

Sadly Clark saw them go. He knew that he had no means of restraining them. He knew also that the quiet was deceptive. At any minute it might be shattered by the same old cunning and unscrupulous enemies.

The winter was bitterly cold, the coldest that pioneer folk could remember. Ice choked the rivers and small streams froze solid in their beds. Cattle and horses perished in their drafty sheds; in the forest wild animals died for lack of food.

There was sickness in Vincennes. Most of the soldiers in Fort Patrick Henry were down with chills and fever. Clark nursed the sick and yearned for spring to come.

During this dull, dark season he was comforted by Richard's companionship and by letters from his brother Jonathan and from his parents in far-off Caroline County. Jonathan was a major in an eastern regiment; he wrote that, with the exception of William, all of John Clark's sons were now serving in the American army.

"*And*," said Richard blithely, "since I've been commissioned as a lieutenant, we're all officers. 'Do justice and fear not'—the Clark motto, George."

"Yes," George said, "so it is."

Spring brought a fresh tide of settlers into the West. The ice thawed and Clark went to the Falls of the Ohio. He was amazed to see that his tiny settlement on Corn Island had become a village. In May a fleet of three hundred flatboats tied up on the river's south bank. The boats were filled with emigrants from the East. And other emigrants were moving to the frontier on foot or in wagons, through the Cumberland Gap, over the Wilderness Road which Daniel Boone had opened.

These people had heard of George Rogers Clark. It was solely because of him that they felt secure in their raw new surroundings. They talked about him and praised him—but very few could be induced to enlist with his troopers.

Things were changing. Clark saw the evidences of change as he traveled across Kentucky and Illinois. In June of 1779 Spain had declared war on England. Spain was not particularly sympathetic with the ideal of American independence; but she did not intend that in the struggle England should rob her of Spanish possessions in the Mississippi Valley. Now there were frequent skirmishes between the English and the Spanish in Florida and Louisiana.

"England is stirring up the Indians to attack the Spanish—and, of course, to take a sideswipe at us," Clark remarked to Richard. "We ought to be looking to our defenses."

143

Patrick Henry was no longer governor of Virginia; he was now a member of the legislature, and Thomas Jefferson was the new governor. Clark would miss his contacts with Patrick Henry, but he had a great respect for Jefferson. When Jefferson asked him to supervise the construction of a fort at the falls of the Ohio, Clark was glad to do so. The fort he built was large and substantial. He named it Fort Jefferson.

The emigrants were building, too—log cabins, trading posts, a church, houses of brick or stone in a circle around the fort. Clark realized that before many more years passed a town would flourish here, and he was determined that it must be a good one. He threw himself into the work of planning the town, which already was being called Louisville. He surveyed the land and laid out the streets, reserving spacious tracts for parks and gardens.

"Louisville must be the most beautiful city on the continent," he told the settlers.

Then he built a house of his own in Louisville; and one night he had a ball there, with fiddlers and dancing, bowls of punch, pitchers of toddy, and the lady guests dressed in their most fashionable gowns.

But always he was thinking about Detroit, wondering when it would be possible to organize his expedition. He loathed this idleness; it worried him. The British were not idle. They were at their old mischief, bribing the hostile tribes to rise and raid again—of that he was sure!

Captain Montgomery, with a small company, was patrolling the Illinois border. In the summer Clark had an "intelligence" from him. The British were descending

144

the Mississippi from the North. They would attack the Spanish in St. Louis, the Americans in Cahokia.

Clark mustered the men of Fort Jefferson. They set off in boats, strained at the oars, hurried down the Ohio, rounded into the Mississippi and reached Cahokia.

Twenty-four hours later the enemy appeared, British officers commanding a horde of Indians. The fighting was sharp but not prolonged. The Indians had a superstitious dread of George Rogers Clark; they believed him to be invincible. They had not expected to see the chief of the Big Knives at Cahokia; his presence there dismayed them and they retreated across the river toward St. Louis.

Clark crossed also, in hot pursuit, only to discover that the raiders had been beaten off and were in flight up through the valley of the Illinois River.

The Spanish had fought stubbornly, suffering seriously in the encounter. Governor de Leyba had been wounded and was dying. The Indians had carried a large number of prisoners away with them.

"I think it is the beginning of a general outbreak, Colonel Clark," said Navarro, de Leyba's Spanish captain.

Clark nodded grimly. "I'll chase the scoundrels and overtake them before they do more damage."

He went back to Cahokia—where a scout had arrived from Fort Jefferson with word of the most disturbing kind. A thousand Indians were swarming like a plague of locusts into Kentucky.

"They mean to invade and destroy all the Kentucky villages," the scout said. "They're whetting their tomahawks, thirsting for blood."

145

"Have the people been alerted?" Clark asked.

"Not yet. To get to them, a messenger would have to go through the woods where the Indians are camping."

"And nobody has done that? Then I'll go."

The scout protested. "They'll spot you, Colonel. They'll be watching for a white face. They'll kill you—"

"I'll pick two men to go with me. We'll paint our faces, braid our hair in scalp locks. Disguised as Indians, we'll get through!"

He was thinking quickly of the two men to select for this exploit. Ben Linn and Sam Moore? Yes, they would serve him well. . . . But how he wished for Bowman now —Bowman with his iron courage and cool judgment!

He spoke to Montgomery. "I'm off, Captain. March your company up the Illinois River valley, pursue the raiders until they've all dispersed, scuttled into their holes—"

Montgomery interrupted. "Colonel Clark, I've been wanting to tell you that I must resign from the army."

"Resign!" Clark exclaimed, frowning. "Not now! You can't resign now. Obey my order, sir, and don't be a fool!"

Montgomery sighed and saluted. "The order will be obeyed," he said.

146

# 16

## ALARM AND COMBAT

Dusty, weary and sweating, the three strange figures entered Harrodsburg. It was noon of a warm summer day. Many people were out and about, but none gave more than a glance at these visitors. Three Indians, they seemed, probably come to trade in the town. And well-behaved Indians were not an uncommon sight, now that George Rogers Clark had made the frontier so safe and peaceful.

The three went straight to James Harrod's door and knocked.

"Jim?" Clark said. "Hey, Jim?"

Harrod answered the knock. "Why, danged if it ain't you, Clark! And all rigged up. What's the game? I never reckoned you'd paint yourself—"

"Never mind that," Clark said. "Jim, we're in trouble."

Harrod swung open the door. "Step inside. Sit down. I'll get you a drink and something to eat, then you can tell me."

As he gulped the water and ate the bread and meat, Clark talked.

"If I could have gone to Detroit last year, this might have been avoided. But no use crying over spilt milk. The British have the tribes with them, more than ever before. They'll hit hard and smash us—unless we hit them first. We've got to have men. A hundred from Harrodsburg—or two hundred."

Harrod scratched his black-bearded chin. "I know of two hundred who could go. Only they won't."

"*Won't?*"

"We've got a government land office here and an agent to register claims. Everybody's land-crazy, hankering to get rich; the office is always crowded. People don't think of the war; they've forgotten it."

Clark jumped to his feet. "Where is the land office?"

"I'll show you," Harrod said.

Clark strode into the cabin which was the land office,

148

presided over by the agent, a plump, bespectacled man in a broadcloth coat.

"Sir," he said, "you must close this office for a while. Your clients have other matters to see to."

The agent gasped. "I'll do nothing of the sort! Who are you? How dare you tell me what to do? I have the authority of the state of Virginia behind me!"

"So have I," Clark said. "You will close this office. And you might as well, or soon there'll be no government land in Kentucky or people to claim it."

The agent scowled and sputtered: "Sir, I'll not argue with you. But neither will I—"

He never finished the sentence, for Clark had him by the shoulder and was pushing him out into the street.

"Lock the door, Jim," Clark said, "and put the key in your pocket."

Attracted by the slamming of the land office door, the citizens of Harrodsburg gathered around Clark. He repeated to them the information he had given James Harrod.

"Enlist with me!" he cried. "Come on, volunteer! Every man that can fire a musket!"

Half a dozen men—a dozen—came forward, but most of them hung back, and a whisper of dissent was heard: "It's not as bad as he makes out. He's exaggerating, spinning a yarn."

Clark shook his head despairingly. They didn't understand, they refused to understand. How could he explain the situation to them?

And at that moment, a courier elbowed through the crowd. The courier was from Ruddle's Station; he was winded, panting.

Yesterday at dawn seven hundred Indians, he told them, led by a British captain had attacked Ruddle's Station. For several hours the settlers had held them off, but then had surrendered. Four hundred settlers had been taken prisoners. The British captain had promised that their lives would be spared, though he would march them to Detroit.

Perhaps the British captain might have kept his promise. But he could not control his Indian allies. Scarcely had the prisoners started on their long march when the Indians fell upon them. Children were torn from their mother's arms, women were scalped, the old and the sick and wounded were killed. Farms were burned, crops trampled, all the cattle stolen.

Revolted by the Indians' cruelty, the British captain had driven his captives toward the mountains, toward Detroit which was four hundred miles distant.

As the courier paused, out of breath, the men of Harrodsburg shouted their willingness to enlist with Clark. They were ready to be soldiers again!

He organized them into companies and appointed officers. In the evening he sent runners to the other Kentucky towns. The runners were to say that a thousand recruits were wanted immediately.

"And I'll get them, Jim," Clark told Harrod. "This will fetch them."

"Well, it's fetched me, anyway," Harrod said. "I'm going."

The Indians retreated when they learned that George Rogers Clark and a thousand armed and angry settlers were at their heels. Clark followed them across the Ohio, then through the Scioto River basin. The region was familiar to Clark. He had been here long ago with Lord Dunmore, trailing the Shawnee.

We'll catch up with them any time now, he thought.

But the Indians still retreated. Clark seemed to them a worker of miracles—stronger than the strongest of the English commanders, or than all the English commanders rolled into one. And he was different from the English, for in his dealings with the tribes he had always been fair. This puzzled them; it was beyond their comprehension. Experience had taught them that fairness was a rare quality in the white man, too rare to be trusted. So they said among themselves that Clark must have supernatural powers; he was either a god or a demon.

In August the Indians were at Piqua, a fortified town on the Big Miami River. There Clark caught up with them, boxed them in and left no avenue open for farther retreat.

Early in the morning the American rifles began a terrific firing from three sides of the town. The Indians returned the fire, shooting from behind trees, barns, cowpens, from the chimneys, roofs and windows of houses. Clark had brought a small cannon with him. As the cannon boomed, his men advanced. The Indians sought refuge in Fort Piqua and sent a rain of bullets over the walls of the stockade.

Through the day the battle continued, the Americans shelling the fort—slowly, steadily gaining ground. At sundown the Indians abandoned the fort and plunged out, trying to escape, singly or in groups, any way they could.

His rifle smoking in his hand, Clark watched the fighting which was now at close range, face to face. The scene was one of utter confusion. Guns blazed, tomahawks and knives swished; a corner of the stockade was in flames, throwing an eerie light over blood-soaked earth. The flames spread, the light flared.

Suddenly someone darted, screaming, out of the fort.

"Don't shoot! I'm a white man! George!—"

Clark stared. The man was dressed like an Indian and he was running straight toward the American line. Clark rubbed his eyes. It was Joe Rogers!

"Joe! *Joe!*"

A gun roared, and whether an American or an Indian pulled that trigger would never be known. Joe Rogers staggered and collapsed. Clark dashed to his side, lifted him up and carried him to a secluded place, where he laid him down again, gently, on the grass.

"Joe, can you hear me?"

Yes, Joe heard his cousin's voice. He was alive—but barely and not for long. In broken words he told of his captivity with the Shawnee, four years of looking and looking for his own people.

"I didn't have a chance to get loose, George," he said. "Not after the ambush at Limestone Creek. Say, did you take the kegs of powder to Kentucky?"

"Yes, we took the powder to Kentucky."

"George, will you write to my folks about me?"

"Yes, I will. I'll write your folks."

Night came, shrouding Piqua in summer darkness. The Indians had gone; they were whipped and cowering; it would be months before they recovered from this stinging defeat. The Americans were caring for their wounded, marking the graves of their dead.

In the riddled fort a candle gleamed. Clark sat there alone, writing a letter to his relatives, the parents of Joe Rogers, telling them the tragic story of their son. Tears scalded his cheeks and dropped on the paper as he wrote.

"Detroit is the hatching place of Indian war," Clark said—and he said it often that winter, to anyone who would listen to him. He was in Louisville; the town was growing rapidly. "But as long as the Indians can be flung down on us from Detroit, we have no security," he said. "The raiding must be stopped, stopped for good!"

The capital of Virginia had been moved from Williamsburg to Richmond. Early in 1781 Clark went to Richmond to see Governor Jefferson. He had pleasant memories of their former meeting, and again Jefferson was cordial to him.

"Yes," Jefferson agreed, "there's no doubt that Detroit is the British key to the western country, the source of all our persecution by the Indians. I have always believed that we should take Detroit from the enemy. And I feel, sir, that you are the one American leader who could take it."

"I could," Clark said. "I can—with some little aid from Virginia."

"I may soon be able to let you have two thousand militiamen," Jefferson said thoughtfully. "And I'll communicate with General Washington, our commander-in-chief; I'll ask him for the loan of cannon and a regiment of troopers from Fort Pitt. It would be well for you to wait here for Washington's reply."

Clark was quite willing to wait; and Washington's reply was prompt and satisfying. "I do not hesitate to deliver to George Rogers Clark the articles requested," wrote Washington.

"These articles must be claimed at Fort Pitt," Governor Jefferson said. "You'll probably have another brief wait—until I can send the Virginia militiamen. But surely by spring your venture can be launched."

With a light heart and with the rank of brigadier general which Jefferson had bestowed upon him, Clark went to Pittsburgh. All his hopes were revived and soaring. At last the tiresome delays were behind him. Almost gaily he walked into Fort Pitt—and there was confronted by new and unimagined obstacles.

The officers at Fort Pitt were jealous of him, disgruntled that he should have been given a commission of such importance. What was he, they murmured, but a reckless, daredevil youth, not yet thirty years old? His ideas were absurd, impractical. An attack on Detroit? How ridiculous!

The officers dallied; they made excuses for disregarding Washington's instructions about the loan of cannon and a regiment.

"Well, I'll go on without them, then," Clark said angrily. "When the Virginia militiamen come—"

They did not come. Just as Clark was voicing his impatience in Fort Pitt, two British armies were sweeping into Virginia. The militiamen were fighting furiously on their own soil, trying to repulse two separate invasions;

not a trooper could be spared for fighting elsewhere.

Jefferson wrote to Clark, advising him to recruit a company in Pennsylvania; and Clark accepted the advice, scouring the settlements around Pittsburgh. Slowly he collected a hundred Pennsylvanians—and very green and crude they were, totally unversed in the rugged ways of the wilderness and Indian warfare.

He was training the men at Fort Pitt when dispatches arrived from Kentucky.

Things were dismal in the West, it seemed. The tone of the dispatches could not have been gloomier! The garrisons at both Kaskaskia and Vincennes had dwindled, the guards quitting on one pretext or another, because they had no money, no decent food, because their clothes were in shreds, their boots worn through—why, the sentries were pacing their posts barefoot!

And at Fort Jefferson the savages were stealthily encroaching; every night showers of arrows rattled on the roofs of Louisville. Farmers in the vicinity could not plow their fields; they were bringing their children into town where the soldiers might protect them. Everybody was fretful, forlorn or quaking with fear.

At the bottom of one dispatch was scrawled a question: "Can't you come back for a while, Clark? You're needed. . . ."

He would have to go back. It was June. He told his new recruits that the Detroit campaign was not called off. Indeed, no! He was merely deferring it until later in the summer.

With a small escort of riflemen he left Fort Pitt for Kentucky.

155

The Pennsylvanians were to obtain flatboats and follow him.

This was the crucial year of the Revolution. American independence would be won now or never.

And it was the time to strike at Detroit, Clark thought, as he rode from village to village in Illinois and Kentucky, placating the settlers; the ripe and proper time, the one opportunity he would ever have—now, in this precious summer, which was fast slipping by.

A month passed and the people of the West seemed less frightened, the Indians less annoying. In the latter part of July he told himself that he could get away, that it was safe for him to leave.

But where were the Pennsylvanians? What detained them?

In August he knew.

The inexperienced officer in charge of them had beached the boats near the mouth of the Miami River to let the men have some hunting. Indians crouched in the tall grass along the Miami; the woods bristled with Indians. Yelps sounded—and within the space of an hour the officer and all but one of the new soldiers had been slaughtered.

They were dead. And Clark knew with bitter certainty that his hopes of the Detroit campaign died with them. He must thrust the thought of it from his mind, hold on grimly to his Ohio forts, defend his territory here, keep the West intact for the Union.

August, the month of falling stars. . . .

At night he watched the stars glittering high above the

river, noticing how some of them flashed for an instant, then slid down the dark sky and vanished. Was he like one of those stars, he wondered? Was it his destiny to drop now from the loftiest heights into darkness? . . .

In the East and South the Revolution was drawing to an end. England was realizing that she had lost her American colonies, lost them irrevocably. At Yorktown, Virginia, on October 19, 1781, the final battle was fought, the massed forces of Washington crushing the armies of the British Lord Cornwallis.

Statesmen representing both nations were already in Paris, where peace negotiations were in progress.

At Fort Jefferson, Kentucky, George Rogers Clark received an official order: No further offensive movements were to be made against enemy troops on the continent.

But the Indians of the western tribes were not impressed by decisions and rules made by a handful of white statesmen. The Indians were a law unto themselves. For them the war was not over. It would never be over until all the ancient wrongs were righted and their happy hunting grounds restored to them.

Ten months after the battle of Yorktown, the Indians besieged the Kentucky settlement near the Blue Salt Licks and laid waste to it. Led by Daniel Boone and Colonel Levi Todd, a small band of Kentuckians hastened to the licks—and into a trap which the Indians had cleverly devised. One third of their number were killed, many were wounded; the rest fled in panic.

Clark had been at the falls of the Ohio when Boone

and Todd met with this disaster. Now the men who returned alive asked him indignantly why he had not gone to the licks. He answered calmly that he was building a new fort and wanted to complete it. Better fortifications on the border were an absolute necessity, he said. To get Fort Nelson built was his most urgent duty.

He added that the conduct of Boone and Todd had been impetuous. They had started for the Blue Salt Licks without plan or caution. Their defeat was due to lack of foresight.

"But of course something will have to be done about the Indians," he said. "That's my job, as commander in the West. And I will assume it."

So Clark mustered his troops and marched boldly into the Shawnee country. At his approach the savages scattered. He fought them in a series of skirmishes and subdued them. Then he marched back to the falls.

He was working again on Fort Nelson when he became aware that more criticism, of a different sort, was being directed at him. Rumors were circulating. Gossiping tongues were saying that he had been inefficient, perhaps even dishonest, about his financial responsibilities and had signed his name to notes on the state of Virginia.

"Did I sign such notes? Yes," he said frankly. "I had to, there was no other way to feed and clothe my men. My own funds were exhausted. I couldn't allow the men to starve, to go naked. I supposed that Virginia would honor the notes—I still suppose so."

But his critics were not silenced. The rumors and gossip persisted; they shocked him and he did not know how to prove them false. He had beggared himself, had unflinchingly faced every conceivable adversity and danger for the sake of friends and comrades.

Was this to be his reward?

Thomas Jefferson's term as governor of Virginia had expired. It was the autumn of 1782, and Benjamin Harrison was the governor.

Suddenly and deeply resentful, Clark wrote to Governor Harrison and asked for permission to retire from the Army.

As he walked out of the fine new fort he had erected on the Ohio, his conscience was clear; he held his head proudly. The people in the Louisville streets would not have suspected that his heart was bruised and aching.

# PROBLEMS OF PEACE

He had never in his life been idle; he would not be idle now. There was much surveying of land to be done for the inflow of immigrants, and Clark became an expert surveyor. Soon he was out tramping the woods and hills, notching trees, fixing property boundaries. He surveyed the site for a town on the Ohio's north bank, just opposite Louisville. The town was to be called Clarksville.

Perhaps, Clark thought, the federal government would someday allot the ground, share by share, to the veterans of his old army.

He built a small log house in Clarksville, on a point of land overlooking the river, and he talked of putting up a gristmill there. He liked strenuous physical labor; it was good for him. It was good, too, to know that he still had many friends; the great majority of the western people would always believe in him.

John Sanders was a resident of Louisville now—Sanders whom Clark had once so sternly reprimanded on the way to Kaskaskia. But long ago that reprimand had been forgotten.

"I'm going into the meat trade, General," Sanders told Clark. "I want you to be my partner."

"The meat trade?" Clark said.

"Yes, sir. The Louisville folks can't get fresh meat. I'm a hunter, I can get it for them. My scheme is to employ other hunters, buy what they tote in to me, then sell the stuff in the market."

"And you would employ me as one of your hunters?"

Sanders laughed. "Oh, no. I want you to invest in the business."

"You flatter me, John. I'm poor, I have nothing to invest. I'm thinking of building a gristmill in Clarksville, to earn my daily bread."

"Well, sir, why can't we be partners in the mill?" Sanders said. "I'll help you build it."

Yet poor as he was, and with his military connections severed, Clark had frequent and varied demands made upon his time in this period. He was named as a trustee of Transylvania Seminary at Lexington, Kentucky, the first school of higher education to be established west of the Alleghenies. He was consulted on matters of government—whether Kentucky should be admitted to the Union as a new state, and about the organization of the vast area of his conquest north of the Ohio River as the new Northwest Territory.

Then, through the influence of Thomas Jefferson, he was appointed as one of seven men commissioned by the Congress to treat with the Indians for a lasting peace on the frontier.

In January, 1785, he conferred with the Wyandotte, Delaware, Ottawa and Chippewa tribes. In the autumn he met with the Shawnee chiefs.

At both conferences he showed his understanding of the red men.

"It is a mistake to load them with presents," he said to his fellow commissioners. "Give them beads and baubles and they think you're afraid of them. Be calm and unyielding and they may consent to deal with you. They are fickle, though, swayed by any wind that blows. The Indian says one thing today, tomorrow something else. These tribes may not abide by the treaties we have just made with them."

But not all of Clark's time was devoted to work. He

162

was a popular guest at the social functions of Louisville. Young, handsome, well mannered, he was fond of music, sports and dancing. It was remarked that more than one pretty Kentucky girl cast flirtatious glances and blushed and smiled when asked to dance the reel with him.

"A pity General Clark doesn't marry," sighed the mothers of the pretty girls. "He would make some lady such a charming son-in-law."

Kentucky was developing, expanding. In the spring of 1785 a thousand flatboats carried settlers down the Ohio. And one of the biggest of the boats brought the Clark family from Caroline County. The Clarks had with them their household furnishing, slaves, cattle and wagons— everything!—for they had come to stay.

The general was at the dock to greet them, his father and mother, brothers and sisters, Jonathan's wife and baby, Ann's husband and babies. What a joyful morning it was!

"The Clarks are a clan, George," Ann said, as she hugged him. "We belong together."

"Yes, George," said William, who was fifteen now, tall and redheaded. "Since you and Richard insist that Kentucky is your home, we'll have to make it ours."

George had claimed six hundred acres of Kentucky land for his father. The tract was on the outskirts of Louisville, a wooded hill topped by a grove of slender mulberry trees. He took his parents to see the land.

"Oh, Mulberry Hill!" Mrs. Clark exclaimed.

George smiled. "Do you like it, Mother?"

"Yes, I do! We must have a house right in the center

of the grove. And you'll live here with us, won't you, George?"

"I will," he said. "And very glad to!"

Several tribes of the western Indians had shunned the commissioners' conferences. In 1786 these tribes joined a group known as the Wabash Confederacy and began once more to terrorize white settlers on the border. It was reported that fifteen hundred of them were encamped around Vincennes. Somehow, mysteriously, hatchets, rifles and scalping knives were being smuggled to them from Detroit. They were preparing for a season of ferocious raiding and destruction.

The settlers were frantic with fear. What resistence could they offer? They might ask the federal government to send soldiers—the soldiers might or might not be sent. But George Rogers Clark was in Kentucky; it would be easier, quicker, to look to him for relief.

They went to the large log dwelling which now crowned Mulberry Hill and begged him to lead an army against the savages.

"We know you to be a champion of the distressed," they said earnestly. "Don't fail us in this extremity."

"I have no army," he said.

"We will get the army!" the settlers declared. "It will not be difficult. Your name alone is worth half a regiment of men."

He was reluctant—yet how could he turn them away?

"Very well," he said, but with vague misgivings.

So he polished his rifle and stuck a cockade of turkey feathers in his old three-cornered campaign hat.

"May I go, George?" William asked.

He nodded. "Yes, though I have a queer feeling about the journey."

"A queer feeling?"

"It may be unlike the others I've made," he said.

By September twelve hundred men were in Louisville. Most of them Clark knew only slightly. They were newcomers to the West, untrained, undisciplined—and opinionated. Some had horses and guns; some had no equipment at all. They argued about the route to be taken, whether they would have enough food, whether to travel to the Wabash by boat or on foot.

Clark told the officers to put a stop to such senseless chatter. But the officers themselves were in disagreement. A few of them said that since Clark hadn't recruited the regiment he had no real hold over it.

He issued an order: a detachment of troops would leave Louisville in boats; the rest would march through the wilderness—with him.

It was a long, fast march—and on short rations. By the fifth day the green recruits were hungry, tired and sullen, grumbling that they had been much more comfortable at their own firesides. By the sixth day the grumblers were deserting, facing about toward home.

Clark saw them and could scarcely believe his eyes. Had they no shame? No grit? He ran among them, shouting and swearing. Like rabbits, they scurried from the sound of his wrathful voice.

When they were gone beyond recall, he mopped the sweat from his forehead and tightened his belt. With those men who remained to him, he marched on into Vincennes.

The French villagers had not forgotten George Rogers Clark. They were delighted to have his garrison of a hundred and fifty Americans in Fort Patrick Henry, and to hear him announce that he would either arbitrate with the hostile tribes or fight them. This was quite like old times, the villagers said.

"But unfortunately we cannot now provide your men with food, sir," they added. "Our crops have been burned in the fields. Our grain bins, cellars and cupboards are empty."

Clark had observed three Spanish merchants in the village. On investigation he learned that the merchants had recently stored several boatloads of corn, beef and clothing in Vincennes warehouses.

He spoke to the merchants. "Did you comply with the shipping regulations for bringing cargoes up the Wabash?" he asked.

"No," the merchants said. "We did not know of any regulations."

"Then your transaction has been illegal," Clark told them. "I shall open the warehouses, confiscate the food and distribute it to these destitute people."

When the villagers and his garrison had been fed, Clark sent messages to the Indian chiefs. He said that if they wanted war, they could have it: "I'll make a conquest of you forever and show no mercy." But perhaps they might prefer friendship; in that case, they must come to the fort and talk with him.

Soon the chiefs were trudging in from their camps to

166

talk with Clark at Fort Patrick Henry. He said that a great meeting to promote peaceable relations would be held at Clarksville in the spring. Would they attend the meeting?

The chiefs said yes, they would attend the meeting.

"And will you halt your raiding during the winter?"

The chiefs promised solemnly: no more raiding.

After four weeks on the Wabash, Clark went back to Louisville. He was optimistic about the spring conference. He began to plan for it. But the plans were never perfected.

In his absence his critics had been busy. New and more severe accusations had been spread abroad. Envious army officers and those men who had deserted him on the march said that his conduct had been highhanded and arrogant. Eastern politicians said that in seizing the cargoes of the Spanish merchants, he had tried to precipitate a war with Spain; in taking possession of the post at Vincennes, he had acted in defiance of the Congress.

Edmund Randolph, now governor of Virginia, published a proclamation condemning Clark's "violence" at Fort Patrick as being unpatriotic.

"The violence," Randolph charged, "was unknown to the Executive. Virginia disavows it."

Clark was bewildered by the storm breaking about his head.

What had he done? Nothing to apologize for—or repent! Nothing he would not do again in similar circumstances!

167

"Unpatriotic"? His one thought had been for his country, his one purpose to gain peace for America.

He wrote to Governor Randolph: "I respect the state of Virginia, sir. . . . Things will prove themselves."

But this second humiliation was worse than the first had been. It was appalling. He knew that he would never shake it off, never rise from its blighting shadow.

168

# 18

# THE QUIET TIME

"I have laid aside all idea of public affairs," George Rogers Clark wrote to his friend Thomas Jefferson.

It was true, and for many months he felt hurt, frustrated, bleakly unhappy. But as the months accumulated into years, and the years passed, the feeling left him. Sustained by the love and encouragement of his family, he was contented with his quiet life at Mulberry Hill.

The days were spent in the performance of pleasant small tasks; his brother William was his boon companion. With William he hunted and fished, studied the trees, birds and animals of Kentucky, tramped through the woods and explored the Indian mounds along the Ohio River.

In the evenings he read—he was discovering the fascination of books. Gradually he collected a library of books of history, geography and natural science. And he wrote innumerable letters in answer to the letters which came to him. His correspondence was voluminous.

In 1789 he was asked by John Brown, Kentucky's delegate to Congress, to write his memoirs—"a narrative of your campaigns in the western country," said the Congressman. The narrative would be of extraordinary value and consequence to the world, and especially to "several of the most important characters in the Union," who were anxiously requesting it.

Clark replied politely to Mr. Brown. He said that he had no knack for literary composition, but would glance through his ledgers and journals and consider what might be done with them.

"If the tale is to be told at all, I guess I'm the one to tell it," he said to William.

"Yes." William said. "No one else knows the details of it."

So he wrote his memoirs, beginning the account with the settlement of Harrodsburg in the spring of 1774, carrying it through the stirring events of 1779—and at that point ending abruptly. He could write of his victories, but not of his shattered dream of capturing Detroit, the reversals and embarrassments which had followed. Perhaps someday he would write the final chapters, or perhaps not. The zeal for putting it on paper seemed to have forsaken him.

He sent the manuscript to Mr. Brown, and the "most important characters" were most appreciative. Thomas Jefferson praised it:

My dear General Clark, you have enterprized deeds which will hand down your name with honor to future times. . . .

In 1779, between the spring and autumn, his mother and his father died. Then he and William kept bachelor's hall in the big log house in the mulberry grove, for the other Clark brothers and sisters were married and had built homes of their own in the neighborhood. The next year William enlisted in the Army. The Indians were still harassing the frontier; since Clark's retirement they had been constantly troublesome. William waited to be called into active service as a lieutenant of infantry.

"Now, George," said his married sisters, when William's call came, "you must move in with one of us. Which shall it be? We all want you."

He smiled and thanked them, saying that he was going to that snug cabin of his in Clarksville: "I'll take three of the Mulberry Hill Negroes—Kitt, Cupid and Venus.

They'll look out for me until William gets back from the border warfare."

William returned to find him engrossed in another chore of writing.

It was 1803 and Thomas Jefferson was president of the United States. At the insistent pleading of George Rogers Clark, Congress had granted thousands of acres of western land to the veterans of his Illinois rgeiments, and was allowing Clark to apportion the individual tracts.

In the front room of his small house above the river, he sat at a table stacked with documents, with more documents stacked on chairs, on the floor.

"See them, William," he said. "Each one is in payment of the government's debt to some old soldier. And long overdue! The men should have had the grants years ago."

"Well, if it weren't for your stubborn disposition they'd never have them," William said. "Better late than never, George. Give me a pen and I'll help."

One day that summer William received a letter from President Jefferson. The letter said Lieutenant Meriwether Lewis and Lieutenant William Clark were to lead an exploration party across the North American continent from the Mississippi to the Pacific Ocean.

William was amazed and jubilant.

"Lewis was in the Army with me," he said. "He's a Virginian, from Albemarle County, and he has been private secretary to Mr. Jefferson. I suppose Lewis spoke up for me. But I'm sure you must have had something to do with it, too, George."

172

"Not much. I recommended you to President Jefferson."

"I thought so! And what exactly did you say?"

"Not much. Only that you are qualified for almost any post of distinction or profit to which you might be nominated. And that it would gratify me exceedingly to have you get such a post."

"Oh, is that all?" William laughed. "The Lewis and Clark Expedition! It will be a great adventure. I wish you were going, George."

"No," he said, "I couldn't. I'm fifty-one—and not as spry as I used to be. You can write to me occasionally. And keep a diary of your trip. I can read about it in the diary."

After he had seen William off on the great adventure, his own existence seemed rather drab and colorless. He strolled around his yard, tended his garden, walked down to supervise the working of his gristmill and have a word with John Sanders. Every evening, whatever the weather, he sat for an hour or two on his porch, gazing out over the Ohio.

From here he could see the falls, the narrow, swirling rapids through which his men had steered their boats as they started for Kaskaskia. He remembered how the sun had been strangely, suddenly, obscured. A total eclipse —and a good omen! From here he had a view of Corn Island, where he had brought those few sturdy pioneers in 1778; a view of Louisville, the town he had surveyed on the river's south shore.

Now again his sisters wanted him to live in their comfortable homes; Jonathan's house was open to him also.

173

Oh, he had plenty of invitations! But he protested that he liked his solitude; he wasn't really lonely. William wrote to him regularly. And he had so many visitors. His nieces and nephews ran in and out of the cabin with the greatest familiarity; they stayed for meals and listened, wide eyed to his stories of the wilderness, the boys leaning against his knees, the little girls clambering into his lap.

Often his old soldiers dropped in for conversation and a glass of cider; and younger men came, too, attracted by his hospitality, the extent and variety of his knowledge of local and national affairs. Sometimes his visitors were Indians, the chiefs of tribes he had befriended—or conquered. To the Indians he was not like other white men; slyness and treachery had never been his weapons. Fairly and squarely he had fought them; they would always refer to him with awe as the chief of the Big Knives.

And once a slim youth with a mane of curling brown hair came to talk to him about birds. That was an interesting day, indeed: George Rogers Clark and John James Audubon seated together on the high, wind-swept porch, eagerly comparing notes on bird migrations in the western forests.

In 1809 he was stricken with paralysis.

It was winter, a cold, cold night. He had been standing before his fireplace reading a newspaper, reading about President Madison, and reflecting that this was the same James Madison he had known at Uncle Donald Robertson's school in Dunkirk—Uncle Donald's clever pupil.

And *I*, he thought, threw my books in the duck pond!

The illness seized him then; he fell unconscious on the stone hearth and his right leg was badly burned.

A surgeon was sent for. The surgeon examined the injured leg and shook his head. The leg would have to be amputated.

Clark was regaining consciousness. "Well, sir," he said hoarsely, "cut it off. Proceed with the amputation."

The surgeon hesitated. "It will be a terrible ordeal for you, General. If there were something I could give you to deaden the pain—"

"Have a drummer fetched, sir. A drummer and a fifer. Let them parade around the house. Tell them to play with might and main. That'll ease me."

A drummer and fifer were summoned. Playing martial music, playing with might and main, they paraded around the house, under the windows of the room in which he lay on the improvised operating table, calm, stoic, uncomplaining. He made no outcry. He seemed contemptuous of the dragging minutes, the agonizing pain, as if he heard in the rhythm of these drumbeats the echo of another drum—hailing him across the flooded prairie to a climax of triumph.

# THE OLD WARRIOR

His wheelchair, padded with soft cushions, rolled very smoothly.

"Here's a corner of the veranda where the sun will

shine straight down on you, George," said his sister Lucy. "A beautiful spring morning, isn't it? This afternoon is your veterans' meeting; the coachman will drive you into town for it. Meanwhile, if you want anything, you have only to shout for me or for one of the children."

He smiled gently at Lucy. She was kindness itself—but then everybody was kind: Lucy's husband Major Croghan, her sons and daughters, the servants in her spacious home. And other people, too. Surely no man had ever been blessed with such relatives and friends. The accident of three years ago had made him utterly dependent on the members of his family. He was sixty now, an invalid, and penniless. Yet they all behaved as if to care for him was a privilege!

He thought of what Ann once had said, that the Clarks were a clan. An accurate description. He wished, though, that he could have managed to pay at least some of the expense of his illness, his board and keep. It would have been only justice—"Do justice and fear not." Well, he couldn't remember a single minute of fear in the entire span of his life; and if he had not done justice, it wasn't for lack of trying.

Sitting erectly in the wheelchair, he was refreshed by the yellow sunshine, the clean breeze of April. Below the house a path wound through Major Croghan's blossoming apple orchard. The apple trees were a riotous mist of pink fragrance. He watched the path, expecting soon to see William walking over from Mulberry Hill to chat with him.

He was very proud of William. That wonderful expedition of Lewis and Clark had been epoch making. In

177

fact, he thought William's contribution to the glory and progress of America far outstripped his own. He frequently said so, while William as frequently contradicted him.

It was the one thing he and William quarreled about. Maybe they'd quarrel about it a bit today—and then be reconciled.

He watched the path, leaned to squint at the figure appearing there.

Was it William?

No, this man was not tall and redheaded. He seemed to be carrying some letters. A resident of Louisville, probably, an acquaintance of the Croghans, coming with mail for Lucy or the major.

The man climbed the steps to the veranda.

"Good day, General Clark."

"Good day, sir." He did not recognize the man, but he bowed slightly, courteously, as was his habit.

"The mail courier arrived early this morning. I noticed these two letters addressed to you, General, and I volunteered to bring them to you."

"Volunteered, eh?" He liked the sound of that! "Thank you, sir."

He watched as the man went back along the path through the orchard. The letters he laid on the arm of his chair. They could wait. Later William or Lucy, a niece or a nephew, would read them to him. Somehow he found reading rather wearing in recent months. At noon the young folks would be coming out to wheel him into dinner. . . . He could hear them now, their voices a cheerful din on the stairs and in the parlor. . . . He

178

waited without impatience, knowing that he would not be neglected.

He must have dozed then and dreamed about the letters, for when he roused he glanced at them. The writing on the flap of the smaller one was thin and spidery—why, it was Francis Vigo's hand!

He broke the tablet of sealing wax and unfolded the letter, reminded as he did so of how Vigo, the St. Louis merchant, at risk to himself had hurried to Kaskaskia with a warning—how with advice and money he had greatly aided in the defeat of Hamilton, the rescue of the Hair Buyer's American prisoners.

Since the war Vigo had lived in Vincennes, a worthy citizen of the new nation. Admiring George Rogers Clark, Vigo had always kept in touch with him. In Vigo's estimate, Clark was a soldier of superlative skill and valor, "the savior of this country," and never discredited, his reputation never tarnished by evil gossip.

"Sir," wrote Vigo now, "accept this plain but genuine offering from a man whom you have honored with your friendship, and who will never cease to put up prayers to heaven that the evening of your days may be serene and happy."

Slowly and gratefully General Clark read Francis Vigo's letter. It was fine. It seemed to lend him strength and a certain vitality—the impulse to open the second letter, which had a Richmond postmark and something official looking in the inky blackness of his name on the wrapper, something portentous in the crackling of the heavy paper.

He read the second letter, rubbed his eyes, read it again, frowning.

Could he be mistaken? Did the stilted language deceive him?

He read it through a third time. No, he was not mistaken.

By an act of its legislature the state of Virginia had granted to General George Rogers Clark a life pension of four hundred dollars a year, and a sword which was already being manufactured for him, with appropriate ornamentations and inscriptions engraved on hilt and blade.

A pension and a sword. . . . Well, he *was* surprised. He could scarcely grasp the full significance of it.

The sword, of course, would be of no use to him. He had dozens of swords, enough for a museum, hanging rusty on the walls of his bedroom. How much better if Virginia could have sent him troops, supplies, funds when he so desperately appealed for them!

But the pension? As he thought of the pension he smiled. The pension was a priceless gift. With four hundred dollars a year he was no longer a pauper, the object of charity.

He supposed that he ought to shout for Lucy and tell her that at last Virginia had remembered him. He must tell Lucy, William, everybody, and write the news to Francis Vigo and all his friends and let them all rejoice with him.

First, though, he would have a moment alone, sitting quite still in sunshine which seemed warmer and mellower than ever before.

180

Inside the house Lucy's boys and girls were singing an old, old song, a song he knew. Softly, under his breath, he hummed it:

*"Green grow the rushes, O!*
*Green grow the rushes—"*

# BIBLIOGRAPHY

Bodley, Temple. *George Rogers Clark.* Boston: Houghton Mifflin Company, 1926.

*Encyclopedia of American History,* edited by Richard B. Morris. New York: Harper and Brothers, 1953.

*Encyclopaedia Brittanica.*

English, William Hayden. *Conquest of the Northwest 1778-83, Life of George Rogers Clark.* Indianapolis, Indiana: The Bowen-Merrill Company, 1896.

Havighurst, Walter. *George Rogers Clark, Soldier in the West.* New York: McGraw-Hill Book Company, Inc., 1952.

James, James Alton. *Life of George Rogers Clark.* Chicago, Illinois: The University of Chicago Press, 1928.

# INDEX